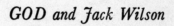

GOD and Jack Wilson

Frederick B. Speakman

GOD and Jack Wilson

FLEMING H. REVELL COMPANY
WESTWOOD · NEW JERSEY

The quotation on page 100 is from "Community Church" from TIMES THREE by Phyllis McGinley.
Copyright 1946 by Phyllis McGinley
Originally appeared in *The New Yorker*
Reprinted by permission of The Viking Press, Inc.

 WESTWOOD, NEW JERSEY • LIBRARY OF CONGRESS CATALOG CARD NUMBER: 65-23619 • PRINTED IN THE UNITED STATES OF AMERICA • 1.1

To Janet, Steve, and Fred,
who might have fared better
as Jack Wilson's daughter and sons,
but who have been kind enough
never to let on.

Preface

Jack Wilson is imaginary, but that does not mean he is not real to me. It means that I stand increasingly in awe of the mysterious bond between imagination and reality. It also means something more obvious; Jack tends to be the man I so often wish I were.

If we have similarities they lie in inevitably shared beliefs and points of view. Jack not only believes that clergymen are bewilderingly human; he is surprised whenever this surprises anyone. He believes that the fundamentals of the Christian faith are vital and alive when they can be talked about in terms most anyone can understand, if they honestly want to. But somewhere near here our similarities break off. You will find Jack able to discuss a belief at some length, apparently extemporaneously, in a manner it would take me some hours to think through. You will often find him saying a thing at the right time, a thing I might think of later and wish I had said. You will find he has an excellent sense of timing with such reactions as anger, an emotional fine art I have never quite developed.

In view of all this, no one should find in Jack Wilson any more of the autobiographical than normally spills over onto the pages of any man's writing. Nor are these chapters meant as a well-rounded and complete discussion of basic Christian doctrine. Every one of these chapters turns on a question I have actually been asked and have wished I had answered better; or on a discussion I have actually been involved in and wish I had conducted more wisely. So, any omissions in theme can be blamed on me, though I'll insist that any arguments with conclusions should be blamed on Jack.

I could not possibly call the roll of all those to whom I am indebted for many ideas that I have worked through the mesh of my own thinking until I think of them as my own. Dr. Carlyle Marney— whose locale is Charlotte, North Carolina, but whose home is the universe—must be mentioned as friend and continuing inspiration. And the late C. S. Lewis is so much with me he is likely to grin or frown from between the lines on every third page. My secretary, Ann Blandford, has been that rare, indispensable person in all the mechanics of manuscript. And I do want to thank Jack Wilson for not becoming, once his freedom was granted him, so independent a person as to take off at a pace that would have left me too far behind.

FREDERICK B. SPEAKMAN

Contents

1

Two Turns at the Fountain

It was one of those foggy days in January when you found yourself shivering, not so much from the cold, since it really wasn't very cold, but from the bleached, gray mist itself that seemed to be everywhere. It smeared the windshield of the car. It streaked over storefront windows. It melted into dismal, oily, little puddles in the streets. It even dripped from the twig-ends of the wet, starkly winter-naked trees.

The Reverend Dr. Jackson Wilson felt soggy himself as he clambered from his car, denting his hat as usual on the awkwardly low overhang of the car door. He shivered and tried to remember how long ago he had taken the two aspirins he was supposed to be taking every four hours. Dr. Barr had said, "There's so much of it around, Jack, and with your schedule, you'd better be on the safe side." It seemed ironic advice. How could you possibly stay on the safe side when that was standard for so much unpleasantness? There's always so much of it around.

But wasn't this a contagiously cheerful line of mood for a clergyman to be reeling out! The fog and mist must be dripping into some part of him that normally refused to turn soggy. Jack took a tug in the belt of his trenchcoat and urned toward the neighborhood drugstore with a stride so deliberate that for him it verged on a swagger.

He smiled to notice how the hard, blue fluorescent lighting of the drugstore interior, ordinarily as cold a light as you could imagine, looked "downright cozy," with a lamp-in-the-window, come-on-in glow in the gloom of the afternoon. The only customer at the soda fountain was a tow-thatched youngster, hunched over to give the final harsh gurgling treatment to two well-chewed soda straws. Catching sight of Jack's clerical collar as he opened his coat, the boy smiled uncomfortably from a mouthful of overlapping teeth —which, God and orthodontists willing, might someday be unlapped—and mumbled some form of "afternoon, Father," and hurried out. Jack had long since given up any effort to correct that greeting. And, after all, he was a father, wasn't he? Three livelier "preacher's kids" had never invaded a manse.

He sat on one of the red, bad-imitation-leather stools and ordered his usual, a chocolate sundae. The girl at the fountain—whose weight, if not a problem, was still not likely to be reckoned as one of her blessings—heaped the chocolate syrup high with a faint expression of disgust which just might have been a mask for envy.

Jack made no effort to conceal his amusement. The only edge of advantage he'd ever felt he had over most of mankind was an inheritance of good health that seemed to require, at least to date, no careful regimen of diet or exercise. He was a man who seemed smaller than he was when dressed. Only at the gym, where he so infrequently worked out these days, would it have been noticed with what measured precision he'd been put together. After all, that was an attribute difficult for a clergyman to advertise. He had yet to meet a pulpit committee which, in going over his knapsack of abilities, had asked him to strip to the waist!

Nicky, the pharmacist on duty, was just emerging from the antiseptic and mysterious jumble of his prescription room. The off-white nylon druggist's jacket he wore looked rumpled and perhaps a size too small, but reassuringly clean. He called across, "Well, I see you've got your work clothes on again, padre." Jack wondered if certain veterans of World War II would ever drop that usage of calling ministers of all faiths "padre." For some reason he hoped they wouldn't drop it; for some reason he liked it.

"You always give the rooster eye at this uniform, Nicky. I consider it a very suspicious reaction."

"That's calling it right. Plenty suspicious. When I see you done up in that collar bit, I know it means one of two kinds of trouble for someone. One kind I've had. The other I'd just as soon not be reminded of. You're like that bad-tooth proverb. Most of the time I can forget it, but now and then it twinges and I know that some day I've got to go through with it."

There was a hint of something beneath the druggist's normal bantering manner which gave Jack that ever-so-slight tightening of the skin along his arms and across his shoulders, a tightening certain voices and certain music and certain apprehensions often gave him. But nothing showed on Nicky's face as he walked over to the fountain and straddled a stool with blunt male inelegance. He reached to finger the flap of a tear in the red cushion of the empty stool between them, then gave it two sudden, clanking, clockwise whirls, each time watching where the flap pointed when it stopped, as if it were some improvised roulette wheel.

Jack had no warrant as yet to allow the tone of his voice

to be other than light. "This weather must have you too, Nick. Have a chocoate sundae with me?"

The druggist's barked laugh was more reflex than amusement. "You and your sundaes! Padre, if I took on that glop the way you do, I couldn't reach the tranquilizer shelf in a month, and we'd really be out of business. No, I wouldn't say it's the weather's got me, but God knows it doesn't help. Just name me anyone an afternoon like this helps."

For an interval that seemed longer than it was, as Nicky sat and stared toward the street, the only sounds in the store were the rhythmic click of his fingernails on the worn marble top of the fountain and a rustling of pages from behind the cash register where the girl had retired to a chair and a comic book, so absorbed in it she moved her lips perceptibly as she read. When Nicky spoke he was still staring toward the windows.

"How do you add it all up, padre? How do you square it all with what I suppose you believe, though I've never talked to you about it—that there's a good God Almighty somehow in charge of this whole business? Oh, I'm not registering my beef in my own name, understand. As I look back, I guess I've never had any real trouble that I didn't ask for. So far, that is.

"But, well—we got the word this morning. I won't give you the full blow-by-blow treatment. Just a family we know over in New Jersey. Daughter's finishing college this year. Wonderful kid! Kind you wish you had. Everything to live for. Marriage planned for June, right after graduation.

"So! There's this wreck on the New Jersey Turnpike this week end. One of those black-leather-jacket crumbs tried to pass her at an idiot speed. It's all over, just like that! College, marriage plans, all that future, all that promise, all over! I know it happens somewhere every hour of the day, that and worse. But this pulled my trigger this morning.

"Of course, the black-leather-jacket kid lived. He'll be fine. I can't tie it in, padre, just can't wrap up what happened so senselessly and needlessly to that wonderful kid. I can't get it into the same package with the notion of a good God somehow in charge of things."

Jack toyed with the spoon in his hand for a moment, as if he were weighing it rather than his words. "Nicky, if the black-leather-jacket crumb, as you called him—if he had been killed in that wreck too, would you feel any better about God? No, now don't snap at me for asking that! You implied it in what you said.

"I believe you've got to decide what it is you're asking. If you're really asking why such a terrible thing should happen to that wonderful girl, then Christianity must take a deep breath and patiently remind you and me that we can't expect God to look at death the way we do. We see it only from this side; He sees it from that side, too. We see it as a door closed; He sees it as a door opened. We see it as the end of a story; He sees it as the beginning of a better story. If there is a God worth mentioning, then this wonderful girl you're mourning has slipped through and far beyond the net of all our little arguments.

"But I don't think you're really asking just about her. I think you're asking, why the needless hurt for those who loved her? Why this pointless heartbreak for her parents, her fiance, her friends? Yes—even, why this terrible involvement for the leather-jacket lad, whose idiocy triggered all the hurt? Because you know as well as I do that he can't come out of such a thing unscarred. If there is a good God who is in charge of life, how could He have let such a thing happen, especially if He could have prevented it? And if He couldn't prevent it, then how dare we call Him Almighty? That's the way the centuries have asked the question. That's the puzzle so bewildering that it's probably a sin for anyone not to be bewildered by it.

"Don't give me that skeptical look, Nick. I mean exactly that. Say, have you ever gone in for jigsaw puzzles? I notice you're selling them again. I hear there's some revival of the fad. Well, did you ever start to work on a tough one, and before you got very far—before many pieces had come together—get the infuriating suspicion that not only were some key pieces missing, but by some crazy accident two different puzzles were packaged in the same box? Two different sets of pieces, one dark picture and one light? All the light pieces look as if they could come together over here in one pattern, and all the dark pieces could imaginably fit together over there in another pattern, but you can't see how the two patterns belong together. Hasn't life ever haunted you with the same suspicion?

"Here's all the love and beauty and goodness, every enjoyable thing, all the truth learned and hope sustained and promise offered, all the hints of some ongoing and eternal meaning that could fit together into the kind of landscape that would be a good God's idea of life. But there's that other set of pieces you've sorted out—the hideous ones, all the apparently pointless pain and suffering and fear that twist lives, the corrosive hatreds and crimes, the threats and terrors of disease and violence, all that could be lumped together as a monster's plan of life, if there were a plan to it.

"Well, which set of pieces is life as it really is, Nick? Why, we know that they both are. You can decide, well, it's a lovely picture, but what puzzle me are the dark blotches. Or you can decide, it's a gloomy, tragic pattern, but what puzzle me are the many bits of light. Whichever way you go, you don't get away from some puzzle.

"Of course, you can say (and it may strike you in your present mood as very high-minded of you to say it) that you can't believe in the goodness of God because of all the evil in life. But even in human reason's little backyard you won't have gained a thing by that, Nick. You've simply exchanged one puzzle for another, another that perhaps is stranger. You're off the griddle smack into the fire. For how, on the basis of no good God at all, will you ever explain the undeniable goodness that's also in life?

"I believe that's one gain faith makes in a time such as ours, when the evils are so dramatic and threatening and obvious. I think we realize something that in balmier ages it's easy to forget: a Christian faith worth having is a lifelong struggle. It's a continual trying to believe. It begins to win its spurs exactly at those points where the evidence is not all clear, where it's by no means uncontradicted. Yes, we've reasons, a variety of good reasons, to believe there's a good God Almighty who is somehow in charge, as you put it. But we're not so pat and glib and easy with those words as we once were.

"By *Almighty*, we mean He is able to do whatever He wills. But He will not be untrue to the kind of God He is, and He will not hedge on His mysterious ways with us. Perhaps as mysterious as any of those is His respect for our right to choose. In fact, His giving us that freedom right in the face of His power may be the neatest trick of creation, the wonder of all wonders.

"And by a good God, Nick, we do not mean a nice God,

not just a sweet God, not even just a kind God. It's so fatal to think of Him as a celestial grandmother whose master plan for the universe is that it can be said by the end of each day, 'A good time was had by all.' We mean something far more important, with far more of the rough, male texture of reality to it.

"We mean that there is One who pays you and me the awful compliment of being in love with us, not because of what we are but because He's that kind of God. We believe He is constantly, sleeplessly maneuvering for our lasting good, even if it costs us our comfort and costs Him pain! He means to have us someday, you see. He means to have us, and He wants us to amount to someone He can enjoy! So we stare at the dark and gloomy pieces of the puzzle, and we don't see how He can bring it off, how He can win—unless we notice that the dark blotches just might come together in the form of a cross.

"Hope I haven't confused you, Nick. No, I think I'll take that back. If you've been taking the goodness of God for granted, I hope I have confused you. Because a God you can take for granted isn't big enough for you and me today."

Jack Wilson slapped fifty cents on the counter and walked to the door. As he glanced out he shivered and tried again to remember when he took the aspirin. Behind him the drugstore was quiet. The girl was still at her comic book. But Nicky the druggist was staring straight ahead, as if, though looking at nothing, he might be seeing something.

2

Night Flight, Tourist Class

Jack could tell by the easy, unforced smile on the face of the airline hostess that the plane would not be crowded. He had a little theory that you could usually guess the size of the passenger list from the degree of warmth in the hostess' smile. If she looked relaxed and even natural with all her poise, it normally meant, "Come aboard, plenty of space." But if her smile seemed frozen tightly to her face, like something put on as an afterthought to her makeup, and if even her words of greeting were staccato quotations obviously memorized from a manual of basic courtesy for airline hostesses, that could mean, "Better hurry, big boy! This plane is either oversold or we'll all just be able to squeeze in like so many chips in a tuna can."

The little rule held true again. Of course, this was a fairly late Sunday-night flight, and it was obvious inside the cabin that no scurried jockeying for seats had been necessary. Most of the window seats were taken, but Jack headed for one of the few still vacant and dropped into it, grateful that now and then some public conveyance provides a chair that corresponds to the basic frame of a rather weary human anatomy. He fussed a minute with the perennial puzzle of the seatbelt buckle, then ran his finger around his neck inside his clerical collar, as if he didn't know from long trying that no such tugging would loosen it. He had meant to change to a soft-collar shirt after the service or in the air terminal, but there hadn't been time.

It was while he fretted with the collar that a man sat down beside him and raised the barricade of a newspaper so deftly there was only a moment for Jack to get the quick impression that if he had to have a fellow passenger, this one seemed to meet a clergyman's fairly specialized midnight requirements: he was male; he was apparently sober; he was of medium build, so there'd be no lapping over the chair armrest; and he seemed not inclined to immediate conversation.

The plane finally taxied to the end of the runway and roared into life there, quivering, determined to free itself from whatever giant grip still held it to earth. Then, suddenly released, it rolled forward and nosed upward so smoothly that to the few passengers who bothered to watch, the ground seemed to fall from under the plane rather than the plane to rise. Then the powerful climb and the lights of the great city shrinking so quickly to toy-town dimensions. As they banked up through one layer of moisture a spray of it squirmed across the windows. But once at flying altitude the air was smooth, and the motors churned their power evenly. The night sky was clear, vastly open to the bright round rock of the moon and those unthinkably far stars.

This was the first moment of a flight Jack could say he fully enjoyed—when the plane was on top, "on the shelf," as he understood they called it. He was irritated to have the moment interrupted by the man beside him, who had folded his paper to look straight at Jack for the first time and say, "Oh, I see you're a minister."

Jack was tempted to answer, "No, no, my throat's been cut. This collar's a bandage." What he did muster was, "Why, yes, as a matter of fact I am. Are you?" It sounded more flippant than he had meant, so he chased it quickly with a broad grin, and it took the grin to change the flash of surprised annoyance in the stranger's eyes to a marked amusement. "No," he said, "no, I've been called a number of things I couldn't be so quick to deny. But one thing I know I'm not. I'm not a clergyman."

He cupped his chin in his hand, a hand that looked rather large and powerful for his size, and stared beyond Jack out the window. Handsome guy. Early fifties? Clear, dark eyes with the crow's feet at the corners just deep enough to soften their intent gaze. Lips tightly compressed, perhaps from some habit of disciplined silence. All in all, it was a deeply responsible if over-controlled face.

"This is a busy season for you ministers, I'd imagine."

"Yes, it's one of our busiest. But why do you say, you'd imagine? Aren't you of a church background?"

Only the man's eyes moved to meet Jack's steadily a moment, then went back toward the window. "Church background? Odd way to put it. That would depend on how far back you want to go. But I suppose you men like to get a stranger located on the religious map as soon as possible.

"I'm afraid I can't help you much as to where to pin me as a specimen. My ideas about religion have always had a hard time fitting together. I guess I've worked at trying not to think about it. But of late, I don't know, it can nag at you, can't it? I've friends who worry because they're unsure of their faith. I find I worry because I'm unsure of my lack of faith. I guess if I had to answer right now, 'Do you believe n God?' I could manage a 'Yes,' and count on God, whoever He is, to know that half of me has always been willing to say *yes*. And the rest of me isn't really hostile, just preoccupied and unwilling to be inconvenienced and frankly put off by such strange claims as your Man from Nazareth routine."

Jack made a mental wager the man wouldn't introduce himself because he found it easier to say what he had said to a complete stranger. That last phrase puzzled him. "Man from Nazareth routine?" he countered.

"Yes, your whole Jesus build-up. Oh, as an art form, as a lovely parable, I suppose anyone could buy it and wish it were true. But it staggers me to think how many of you here in the twentieth century really believe it."

Jack shook his head. "I'm honestly sorry, sir. I'm missing connections with you somewhere. What is it, specifically, that I'm supposed to believe which so staggers you?"

"Why, your whole pitch, that God Almighty once turned into a Man. That the human race managed to get itself visited by a Man who turned out to be God Himself? That—that is what you still teach, isn't it?"

To the other's surprise Jack smiled as he answered, "Good for you. Good for you. You don't believe it, and yet you have thought about it, haven't you? And you're not afraid to put it in so many words. You'd be amazed how many of us who think we're Christians would duck and run before we'd put it in so many words. Not that I'm at all sure you've put it in the right words, or even the best words. But, after all, who can?

"Look, Mr. Whatever-Your-Name-Is—and I won't pry for that. I'll even remain anonymous myself, which is a chore, believe me, for a preacher! You could have noticed me a moment ago, staring out the window, down at the earth then up at those stars, and all that we call space. Don't you think it staggers me to try to wrap my imagination around the claim that the Mind, the Power that arranged all of it ever showed up among us, somehow, in Person? I can say I believe it and I do say I believe it. But I've got to have some ground rules as to how to go about imagining it.

"First of all, I'm not required by the Christian faith to believe that when Jesus Christ walked the earth He was al of God there is. You hinted that in the way you put it. We don't claim the all-knowing Almighty was by some cosmic magic shrunk down to capsule size, small enough to inhabit the Man from Nazareth, so He could seem to be one of us. That would have made of Jesus a monstrous someone, an omniscient, omnipotent young carpenter!

"Look, when Jesus prayed, He wasn't talking to Himself. Remember, those who finally, and to their amazement, knelt to call Him 'my Lord and my God' were first attracted to Him by how much of a Man He was. I suppose the mystery we traditional Christians find hardest to keep in mind is that in all this troubled, dusty, sweaty, painful business of being alive, as Carlyle Marney says it somewhere, Jesus Christ never pulled rank on you and me. When He couldn't sleep, His eyes ached the next day, the same as ours. When He worked too hard for too long, He got tired too. When He missed a meal, he was hungry. When a splinter scratched His arm, He bled. When a close friend of His died, He wept—remember? He had the same for-the-time-being dependence on this little physical machine, with all its weakness or weariness or illness, that you and I have. That's why it took even those who lived with Him night and day, for years, so long to come to the startling conclusion that there

'as something more to Him than His complete and magnifi-
ent humanness.

"Remember, when we talk about the deity of Jesus, we're ot assuming that the Visitor from Nazareth was all of God here is. What we are claiming is that, somehow, in this Ian, God Himself showed up.

"Try it this way. Did you ever, as a youngster, play with a urning glass? Were you ever intrigued by light focused hrough a so-called magnifying glass? Was there ever a low, sunlit, summer day when all the world you could see vas drenched with sunshine, everything soaked in that life-giving gold, unless it was some color of tree or some patch of grass too blue a green to take any gilding, and even that owed its vividness to the light that was everywhere? But vasn't it an acceptable part of that sunny day, no violation of the way things are, that you could take a little glass and hold it just so and concentrate that light, focus it on a wisp of straw or a crumpled paper till it burst into flame? Sunshine everywhere, but here so focused that it burned, and you knew what concentrated light did, and how it acted.

"Look around the universe. The mind of God, the power of God, the inexhaustible activity of God is everywhere. Oh, He isn't the biological act by which we came to life out of the darkness. He is not the meat we eat nor the music we enjoy. He is not the beauty which beckons to us or the friends who keep us better than we are by believing we are better than we are. But it is because of God that all such things can be. So remember the sunshine—does it do violence to God's everywhereness to believe that He could so focus Himself in one life that in that life we can see what sort of Person He really is?

"I know it's quite in vogue today to feel dizzied when we

face a sky full of stars, knowing even what little we know. What a far reach the Creator-God has, such colossal yet coordinated immensities of design! So far a reach that our missiles seem paper-match flares by comparison, and when you hear us talk offhandedly about conquering space, you want to say, 'Not so fast, little man. That's a big word, *space*. That's a huge creation out there!' But the Nazarene story says that God isn't exiled out there in space; He isn't lost among His own stars; He isn't caught out there directing traffic in the unmeasured vastness. He has a near reach too. We're so like that friend Jesus asked, 'Don't you get it yet, Philip? I've been with you all this time, and don't you get it? When you've seen Me you've seen the Father.' Staggering, yes, but thinkable! God Almighty is the same sort of Person as Jesus Christ—always has been, always will be the same sort of Person. You scan the stars or you study the atom to see what He can do, but to see who He is you look—."

All the lights in the plane had gone on, and there was the announcement. They were coming down for a landing. Jack couldn't believe it. He glanced at his watch. "I'm so sorry, I didn't mean to monopolize—."

The stranger's look of disappointment canceled the apology. "Are you getting off here?" he asked.

"Why, yes, aren't you?"

"No, no, I'm going on. Tell me, how long have you boys been teaching this?"

"Why, ever since the New Testament, in one way or another. But, please, don't blame the Book for our ways of saying it. Remember, the movie is never as good as the Book."

There was a moment of hesitation as the plane held its

breath while the runway lights reached up to meet it; then the solid lurch of the tires against concrete as the plane sighed its relief. The man didn't speak as Jack clambered across him awkwardly into the aisle.

Outside Jack glanced back at the great plane, and from one absurdly tiny window someone waved a hand. Had that been their window? If so, what did the waved hand mean?

God help us, Jack thought, you talk, and you talk, and you talk, and you talk, and you never quite know if you've said the right thing at the right time. The man had said he was "going on." Wonder how far? Wonder where? This wistful twentieth-century man, above the clouds, in those far, wide-open skies.

3

Some Other Mirror

For those few seconds after he awoke, those seconds which always seem far longer than they are, Jack wondered why he had been allowed to sleep so late. There was a nine o'clock feeling in the bedroom, not the early morning feeling when the air has been ripped apart by alarm clocks. Then suddenly he remembered why he'd been allowed to sleep so late, why Jo Ann would be waiting downstairs in the kitchen, ready to short-order his breakfast at the first sound of his shower.

Today was his birthday, his forty-sixth birthday. Not too much would be made of it—he'd not allow too much. But this leisurely awakening, and breakfast with Jo at the kitchen table, was a birthday luxury that by now had become a family ritual. Jack had never managed to turn it to Jo's advantage when her turn came. Whatever his abilities, cooking was not one of them and he had never honestly been able to muster embarrassment over the fact.

His shower was hot and brief, but long enough for him to feel all the leftover lethargy of sleep, and perhaps all the conscious fragments of unremembered dreams, wash off with the soap and slosh down the drain. As he rubbed down with his beach-size towel, Jack wondered if there were many men who really would be willing to return to a simpler way of life if that meant surrendering shower baths.

He had no thought of his birthday again until he faced his shaving mirror. The Reverend Dr. Jackson Wilson was no more narcissistic than the next male, perhaps a little less, but this seemed a compelling occasion for some kind of physical inventory. Yesterday "forty-six years old" hadn't seemed so startling; today it seemed no older, only a matter of too many years to be true. Turn around four times and there came fifty. Did a man's age ever sound as old yet seem as young as it did to the man himself? In which of his forties had Vachel Lindsay been when he wrote his birthday lines about hearing the crickets chirp that day—and he was certain they were chirping—"Three months till frost"?

Yet what could a man really learn from his own physical inventory? What could a man really see in his own mirror? The chest and arms and shoulders he saw reflected so matter of factly seemed to Jack neither distinguished nor depressing. The shoulders were broad enough, at least when he remembered his posture. The arms looked strong enough for his size, though Jack retained a boyish annoyance that there was not an inch or so more of biceps. The encroachment of the middle years had not yet fleshed out to erase the punctuation of the rib cage. So, what did all this say?

The face in the mirror was not a face to be remembered from first sight. The jaw was strong; the mouth a straight line, perhaps a trace too wide; the ears seemed not quite as large as they were from lying flatter than the norm against the head; the hair was cropped and could be seen in closeup to be thicker than it seemed at a distance because so heavily salted with gray. Only the eyes, at least so he had been told, were the clue that always gave him away: so dark a brown that at certain angles they looked black, the were an index to his every mood. Tenderness, annoyanc amusement, anger—whatever he felt spilled from his eye however impassive he kept his face. They were twin dar question marks at the moment.

What did this face tell? Would the lines on his forehea have been fewer or more had his name been Jones and h profession law? Would his under-eye circles have bee deeper or lighter had his name been Smith and his practic medicine? Where do you look on a man for his name Where's the tattoo of his identity?

Suddenly Jack laughed aloud in self-amusement. Ho could he have tricked himself into this charade of sel inventory without remembering until now. In one of th earliest of the do-it-yourself charm-and-poise books writte in America, a key exercise suggested for winning self-assu ance was that early in the morning, and again just befor retiring at night, the reader was to stand before his mirro square his shoulders, look himself admiringly in the eye, an repeat his name slowly, a dozen times or so, in a gentle, lov and pleased tone of voice, in order to impress himself wit himself! And in a flash of quite unconscious humor th author had footnoted the warning that when this winsom exercise was performed late at night the student must co centrate and be careful not to doze off to sleep!

How could he possibly have forgotten? He could remem ber so clearly how the first chapter of that absurd book ha closed with an illustration beneath the concluding para graph, a line drawing of a young woman seated at he dressing table, elbows propped on the table top, chin res ing pertly on her clasped hands, staring intently at the re flection of her face in the mirror. Jack remembered ho he had laughed and even said aloud to the girl in the draw ing, "Careful, lady, don't go to sleep! If it's your own name you're repeating in a voice gentle, low, and pleased; or if you're on a wiser errand; or even if you're asking who you really are from the mirror, mirror on your wall—still, be careful, and don't go to sleep! Because we can't see who we are in our own looking glasses, with our own faces staring back at us. That's a search that takes some other mirror."

Yet it was only a laughing matter when it was pulled out of focus. For isn't that a longing that drives every one of us, whether we realize it or not? And anyone who has ever sensed it clearly enough understands why the Christian faith sees so much of the basic human predicament, so much of every man's riddle, in George Macleod's story of an evening in an army encampment in England shortly after the Second World War. The men were killing time, waiting to be mustered out, and a boxing match had been arranged between two companies of soldiers. After one bout, and before another began, a doctor helped a soldier, an amnesia victim, crawl through the ropes and led him to the center of the canvas of the improvised ring. He stood there, turning, so that all could get a look at him, this husky, clean-featured but rather pale lad with a puzzled, searching look on his face. In the hush that slipped over the crowd he asked simply, "Isn't there anyone here who can call me by name? Isn't there someone here who can tell me who I am?"

That's a question we all go through life asking, in one way or another. It's all tied in mysteriously with what we mean by "the fall of man"—that strange loss of memory, that loss of our identity, that forgetting of our name. It was in such a different world climate than ours, back at the turn of this century, that G. K. Chesterton talked about this abiding human predicament in a way that's as valid today as then. Chesterton's conversion to Christianity had amazed some of his friends, such as G. B. Shaw, and they laughed. Oh, they had learned, even Shaw, not to let their laughter be too loud or too long, for there simply was no mental trigger-man in England who could outdraw or outduel Gilbert Keith Chesterton. They laughed at his serious acceptance of what they called "those absurdly outmoded myths of God's creation of man in God's image, and this business of sin which had distorted and defaced that image." And Chesterton answered that he didn't care too much what they called it, so long as they were honest enough with the evidence to admit that they were talking about something that is real to all of us.

Something did happen to us all, long, long ago; and whatever it was, every man has forgotten who he is! So life barks at us, "Thou shalt love the Lord thy God but thou shalt not know thyself." We're all amnesia victims. We have all forgotten our names. And what the world calls common sense and practicality means that in the routine of our days we can "forget that we have forgotten." And when the best in us flowers into art and poetry and beauty and love, it means that for a moment we almost remembered—at least, we remembered that we have forgotten.

Whisper your name to your mirror, sweet and low? What name? What is your name? Who is there to tell you who you are? It is hard even to remember that we've forgotten in the hurricane winds blowing through our world today, the winds it takes such strength to stand against. It's so much easier to run with the winds, to let whatever is happening go on happening. It's so much easier not to think too much and to be cued like a billiard ball to careen off of trouble or nonsense and roll in whatever direction our day tries to aim us. Yet we can't quite stop thinking; we can't quite stifle the gnaw of the riddle, the mysteries that whisper to any man who ever takes a moment to say quietly, "My life, what is it? I have me on my hands, but who am I?"

You, without so much as a by-your-leave, were summoned out of nowhere by an act of flesh and spirit in that logically impossible, that actually quite unreasonable miracle of birth. Some tiny cells carried over their tiny bridge of inheritance what an amazing weight of possibilities, selected and passed on to you from others back up the years. So you're launched on a haunted journey, haunted by invisible things that have never bothered the tiger or the eagle or the mole. You're haunted by memories and by desires and by a light that turns on inside us called "self-consciousness." You're haunted by loves that turn out to be so much more than physical, and guilts that turn out to be so much more than fears. You're pulled at by yesterdays that are gone, but reached for by tomorrows that haven't yet appeared—through hours where loveliness walks arm in arm with tragedy, and laughter was born a twin and the twin's name is tears, and ugliness is blindingly real but so is beauty—and you can't explain away either happiness or heartbreak because, mixed as they are, they're both here. And that clay house of a body you inhabit, the one you can feel so proud of on Mondays, Wednesdays, and Fridays, but the rest of the week feel trapped in. And there are so many more ways to go wrong than to be right, and so many more ways to fail than to succeed. Yet you go on, if sometimes only in your dreams, as if you knew you are under higher orders to struggle and love and hope and try to accomplish.

What sort of talk was this? Poetry? Whimsy? No. Theology. For this is the way we are, we who don't know who we are.

All the while there is One who can tell us. There is One who all our lives has tried to tell us our names. In the chaos of voices hooting at us that we're no one, that we have no name, that we're much ado about nothing, He has urged us to remember that we're much ado about God!

There is that about you which is a truer clue to who God is than an atom or a tree or a toad or a star could ever be. There's a family resemblance. It's just about buried, but it's there! Dust of Eden, made in His image to be a living soul—that doesn't mean we are little models of God; it doesn't mean we are, in any way, little carbon copies. Of course, you'll meet those who are determined to believe we believe that, so they can promptly punch prearranged holes in it. It simpy never has meant that.

It means that your secret is that the only One who can tell you who you are is the God you belong to, the God who created you uniquely to respond to Him, the God who created you in freedom but has given you fair warning He'll be after you all your life to try to claim you as His.

That's why the other mirror, the other mirror we keep forgetting to look into, is Christ. There we see, not at first, our face but His Face, and we know "both our weakness and our worth." We see how we have failed, but also how we are loved. We see how we have rebelled, but how gladly we are forgiven. And in time, as we really learn His name, we will know our names. The world is old, and the stars are old, and trouble is old, and sin is old, but He is forever young and always here! And no man, not one of us, has quite as much time to look around for Him as he thinks he has, does he? Perhaps that's about all there really is to a birthday—to remind us of that.

Jack turned on the hot-water faucet and reached for the shaving cream. Perhaps that's about all there really is to your own mirror. A man can wash his face by it, and shave.

4

If You Think Three's a Crowd

"She's a very bright woman," several people had told him. "Whatever else you may hear about her, you'll find her a very bright woman." They hadn't been specific as to all the "else" he might hear, and Jack felt quite uninformed by the word "bright." After all, that could mean "intelligent," or it could run in pack with some such combination as "bright, brash, and brassy." And he had had no chance to decide before tonight.

Over a period of several years he had met her, at the most, half a dozen times, and always at one of those larger-than-life-size occasions which we call "social" when we mean "superficial." Everyone's on stage, and everyone's mask is screwed on tight, and everyone's set to say not what he thinks but what he thinks the others think he thinks, and to seem to be what he imagines all the others imagine he is. And the conversation goes on like a third-rate game of lawn tennis from the eighteen nineties: I serve it to you where you can reach it, and you knock it back to me where I can reach it, pat, pat, pat, pat. The rule of the game is that you never go beyond the obvious, and everything's smooth and easy.

If at such occasions this woman seemed to play the role of just another of our bright, brash, and brassy contempoaries, that was warning enough to keep any verdict open, since no one in the world is only another anything. There certainly was a flash of something more here tonight as he stood near the fireplace talking to her face to face, even though their first remarks had been a routine skirmish in the suburbs of the platitudinous.

Close up, Jack found her strangely more yet less attractive than from across the large room: more because face to face you could appreciate her careful grooming and excellent taste; yet less, because for all her unarguable femininity, there was a look in her eyes and a line to her mouth that was normally associated with a man's face. Her eyes were a cold rather than a warm blue, and that set of the mouth would have fitted a much squarer jaw line. It was a mouth that would seldom smile, yet never pout. It was a knowing mouth that seemed not to care much for what it knew, yet not to expect to learn more that was much better.

Jack was almost prepared by this appraisal for the bluntness with which she, without preface, suddenly let him have it. "I always like to ask you ministers in the more traditional churches—if you're doing any thinking on your own—how comfortable are you with the old notions of the Trinity? I know that in my own little corner of the room, to make sense of even one God takes some doing. But, brother, three's a crowd!"

He had a moment to catch his mental breath at the unexpectedness of the gauntlet she'd tossed down, for their hostess came charging down on them, cooing like a bilious pigeon, as Shaw might have put it; whether to protect her friend from the clergyman or the clergyman from her friend, Jack decided he'd rather not know. Apparently reassured, their hostess sailed away again.

As Jack offered the woman a chair and then seated himself

he found his thoughts racing. Wonder how many of thos who worshiped regularly with him each Sunday would hav to second her refusal to take seriously our classic naming o God as Father, Son, and Holy Spirit? How many considere those names just another of the ways preachers talk i church? They're used to it; it no longer bothers them. The asked some questions about it when they were youngsters but the adults who answered them either seemed glib wit their answers, or tossed it back as one of those "mysterie you'll understand better when you're older." And yet the seemed uneasy, these adults, about being asked, as if thi were one of those things you really didn't talk about. So how many, Jack wondered, had let it go at that ever since How many, if they were pushed, would have to confess certain impatient confusion which still lingered, and whic could find voice in this woman's sharp, "In my little corne of the room, to make sense of even one God takes som doing. But, brother, three's a crowd!"

She was lighting a cigarette, holding the filter betwee her teeth in an odd and, he suspected, calculated manner Jack began, "Well, I'll try to speak to that, if it's understoo I don't speak from any stance of attempting to clear it u once for all. I long ago made my peace with the fact that a God who could be neatly packaged and fully explained wouldn't be a God worth having, just as a life that could be thoroughly understood might not be a life worth living.

"What I think I'd offer first of all would be a warning. It would be that you and I could make the Christian faith much easier and much simpler if it were something we were making up—if it were something we were inventing, sitting at the drawing board of life, commissioned to turn out a religion tailor-made to our thinking and our preferences, patterned to fit exactly the kind of God we'd like to believe in. Why, we could come up with a very attractive and reasonable religion, neatly geared for the consumer trade! After all, anyone can be simple, if he has no sticky, troublesome, jagged-edged facts to bother with.

"But you and I didn't invent Christianity. We aren't making it up, and we didn't originate its age-old claim that it is concerned with facts, all facts, troublesome or not—that it's based on what is really real and always has been real and always will be real. When we go fishing in that stream we've no right to expect that all the answers we get will be simple. That has always seemed to me to be a trap some of our best thinkers have fallen into. What right do we have to expect that the Reality which brought all the paraphernalia of this life is obligated to make Itself fully explainable or understandable to us?"

Her face was expressionless and her eyes still cool, but she was listening; and if you're going to be presumptuous enough to start preaching at parties, how much more encouragement can you ask?

"That, then," he went on, "by way of a warning. And I suppose this should come as some sort of reminder. If you're going to put your objection to the Trinity as you just phrased it, then there is no Christian answer to it! 'Three's a crowd!' That's cute, if you'll forgive me, but it's so far out in left field that you must come back into the dugout and start the game all over again. Of course, three Gods would be a crowd; and Christianity isn't interested in, isn't buying any of that brand of pagan confusion. No matter how strange it may sound, the Trinity is our way of trying to make sense of one God. The Trinity is Christian shorthand for saying 'I believe that God the Creator is the very same God who is seen and known in God the Son and the very same God who is sensed and felt in God the Spirit.'

"And when people object, as they have for centuries, 'What an awkward, clumsy way to say it!' we can only reply that we'd rather be awkward and clumsy in the direction of reality than glib and clever in the direction of nonsense. When they say, 'but you're just playing with words,' we can only answer that we don't believe we are. But we'd rather play fast and loose with words than play fast and loose with life. That's what seems to be forgotten when the Christian Trinity is mentioned. It grew out of life; it had its beginnings in some observations most of us can come up with if we'll only poke around awhile in the storeroom of our own experience.

"To begin with, you have to trick your mind, force it, drug it habitually with bootlegged doubts, twist it off the hinges of its given pattern of thinking, in order for you to avoid some kind of belief in God the Creator of this universe. Of all the wild improbabilities that have ever been offered us as a so-called explanation of creation, surely the wildest and most incredible is that there simply isn't any planning power behind it all—that it all came from nowhere and for no reason whatsoever! That an uncountable number of tiny bits of senseless matter just happened to be churning around in the emptiness of space, and just happened by a billion freaks of chance to come together in such a way as to arrange themselves into planets and atoms and tigers and trees and poetry! That deep in the seas, where no eye of ours can go probing, those senseless bits of matter just happened to produce creatures with shells as balanced and beautiful in structure and design as any master artist ever could have conceived! That they just happened to put the colors in the sky at dawn or in the peacock's tail! And then, that this senseless matter just happened to produce people. Is this the explanation of minds that have been thrusting at nature to measure its laws, or the symphonies of Beethoven and the clear trumpets of Purcell, or blind Homer's verse and Shakespeare's with his eyes wide open, or the hand of a Michelangelo, or the Parable of the Good Samaritan, or that touch of the truth beyond time that juts into time in the Parthenon and the Taj Mahal and the Lincoln Memorial? Was all this just one big senseless accident, something that happened to happen that way, with no more meaning in it or purpose to it than the accidental bubblings of some vast mud pie? I think it was Dr. Fosdick who said, somewhere, that to believe that explanation simply takes more gullibility than most of us can muster.

"It makes so much more sense to assume that whatever name you give it, there's been some planning Power, some great Architect, some kind of master Designer behind all this display of such ingeniously coordinated immensities. Since it's very difficult for us to think of purposes without a mind planning them, and just as difficult for us to think of a mind as an "it," most people have had their version of belief in some God the Creator.

"But that really doesn't say too much about Him, you see. Thinking only that far, you're not at all sure that He would have coming to Him any more than the forced and fearful respect you'd grudgingly grant any cosmic bully that big! What's more, He has turned out, at the same time, a good many things that are certainly not character references for this Creator. We've seen what stares out at us from the beady eyes of the cobra, and rustles with the tarantula, and lurks in the death bite of a virus so tiny we can't see it.

Earthquakes and hurricanes, cholera and cancer, crippling ills that strike before birth, madness that we still may discover is as much a matter of blood chemistry as short-circuited emotions, a welter of crazed lust and destruction and war—are these His doing, too? What face are we to imagine this Creator wears up there among His stars?

"Ah, but you see, there's something else at work on you and me in the dressing room of our experience. Not up among the stars, nor in the depths of the seas, but at work on you and me in the intimacy of our own hearts is something inescapably personal. Sometimes it speaks to us from beauty, till our eyes are wet. Sometimes it whets our hunger for truth, whatever the cost. So often it is felt as an inner marching-order for us to live a certain way. H. G. Wells used to swear at it and call it "This idiotic feeling I have in the dark that Someone keeps trying to get in touch with me." Thomas Wolfe, for all his driven doubts, described it simply as "Someone who speaks my name in the night." Thomas Hardy, with all his angry and determined agnosticism, could not explain away his feeling that "There is a power in life that personally cares for me."

A tribal chieftain told a missionary in the bush, "We've always known that after sunset Someone brushes by us as He walks among the trees, but we have not known enough to speak of Him." In the Far East an oriental peasant told another missionary, "Oh, I've known Him, I've known Him all my life. I've just never known His name."

"Some Power wants us to do certain things and not do others. Some Power wants us to pray. Some Power wants us to reach out and bless others, not just use them. Some Power wants to empower you and me to hope and trust and go on seeking.

"Who is this Power? Why, we answer, this is God, too! But which God? Why, the only God there is, the same God who fashioned the stars. What? Do you mean to claim that that vast One could be so aware of me as to keep trying to be the very determining core of my life? Yes, that's exactly what we claim. But how is that possible? Well, you know, that's one we don't have to answer, thank heaven, because that one is really beyond us. We don't have to know how He so set fire to the sun that a single grape might ripen on a vine as if it were the only grape on earth, or how He stays at work in our hearts.

"But how can we possibly tie the two together, that vast Creator and this seeking Spirit? Why, they came together once, right before our eyes, to show us that they are not they, but one. They came together in the Man from Nazareth town, who focused all of God Himself that a life here among us could contain. It's to Him we look. Christ is the unique and supreme religious fact, and He identifies all the rest of the evidence.

"We believe that God the Creator is the very same God who is felt and sensed in God the Spirit, and that each is a version of the very same God who is seen and known in God the Son. We believe you can't say what has to be said about God unless you learn how and why to use that one God's three names.

"How can we believe that the Creator's power has a Father's heart and spirit? Why, we have seen His Galilean face."

5

The View From the Curb

He resisted the childish impulse to kick the car when he tried to start it again. The battery was still as dead and unresponsive as last month's household budget. But, after all, it was no deader than when he had tried it thirty minutes before, and he wasn't quite sure what mechanical magic he had hoped might revive it in that half hour. The service station had insisted curtly that they couldn't possibly be there for an hour or so. Jack walked around the car and eyed last year's model with the wry balefulness he reserved for all mechanical things that wouldn't work. He had often wondered how people who understand engines feel about engines that won't go. At least they probably have some theory as to why not.

Jack belonged to that sizable group of mystified mortals who have no notion of why a car ever goes in the first place, let alone why it should ever refuse to go as long as it is regularly fed on the high protein of state-taxed gas. He felt the same personal resentment he always felt toward knotted shoelaces that wouldn't untie, and pencils that snapped their leads off for no explainable reason, and nails that, instead of going in straight at the first smack of the hammer, deliberately bent over on their sides. He had long ago typed himself as one of those for whom it simply could never be a do-it-yourself world, because of the malicious perverseness of inanimate things whenever he took a hand. It was all very well for St. Paul to talk about himself as a tentmaker—wonder what sort of needle he used, and whether he could thread it himself!

Well, nothing for it but the bus. He certainly couldn't justify the expense of a cab for this meeting on the other side of the city, even though he'd be noticeably late.

As he turned from the parking lot to cross the street to the bus stop, he found himself smiling. Just by crossing the street he could feel his annoyance and peevishness drain out of him like water spilled from a basin. It was the weather, of course, this magnificent weather that had finally come, invading even the defenses of the city, and bringing out, almost overnight from the same hybrid seed, the lawns, the flowering shrubs, and the street-repair crews.

What weather vanes we all are, Jack thought. Back in the church study some part of his mind might have protested that there was to be no lingering spring this year, that winter was dying so hard, and suddenly it would be summer. But there wasn't any sustaining a protest in the full of this warm morning, with just enough breeze and just enough bunched screening of white cloud to pattern the welcome sunlight into massive slanting bars of solid gold.

The only man waiting at the bus stop was staring across the street at the church. He turned at the scuff of Jack's shoes on the curb, turned to give him the quick impersonal appraisal which seemed more a matter of habit than interest. Looking at Jack's suit and tie before he even glanced at his face, he announced by way of greeting, "If you're taking the Oakwood bus, we've just missed it. Means a twenty-minute wait, if they're on time, which they never have been yet." It was not said grumpily or resentfully, but as a matter-of-fact acceptance of the kind of world we live in.

The man was taller than Jack, conservatively dressed, lean, with a thin mouth and straight nose. It was a face that had gone a few tough rounds with life and hinted at rough treatment in the clinches. His fingers were inclined to drum nervously on the sides of the briefcase he kept shifting from hand to hand. He reminded Jack vaguely of an economics teacher he had once had, though this specimen boasted a little less hair and a little more chin.

He turned now to wave a hand at the church across the street, and announced flatly, but again without rancor, "That's an ugly church there, isn't it?"

Jack let his surprise do duty for a moment's full consideration before he answered, "No, not to me. To me it's a beautiful church."

The man turned on him with that blunt appraisal again. "It isn't your church, is it?"

Jack hedged, "If you mean, Did I build it? or, Does it belong to me?—again, no."

"Then I don't see how you can say it isn't ugly! It's an American jumble of some kind of Gothic, isn't it? Look at it looming there, all dark stone in a bright morning, taking up valuable downtown property. What business does it have in the middle of an American city, still trying to say whatever it was some half-civilized Goths thought they were saying fresh out of the forests of Europe five hundred years ago? What has that to do with the twentieth century? I like to see a church that's gleaming white and simple. You know, the New England bit. At least it does something for the view."

Jack countered, "But by your reasoning, what business would it have there, trying to say whatever New Englanders were saying two hundred years ago? What has that to do with the twentieth century? But I won't argue architecture with you. Just remember, Gothic churches were never meant to speak their piece through a view from the curb. In fact, no church is. I like them in a landscape too, but a church can never be seen except through the view from inside. By the way, while we're on the topic—do you consider yourself a Christian?"

It was the other man's turn to hedge. "That always depends on who's doing the asking."

Jack laughed with genuine enjoyment. "You are so right; that is, if you realize that finally neither you nor I are doing the asking."

The man removed his hat again to mop his forehead against the mounting heat of the morning. He replaced the hat at an angle that went with the jut of his jaw, by way of warning that he was about to speak his mind. "Look, waiting for a bus is no time to argue religion with strangers. But I've decided lately to speak out whenever my hand is called.

"Yes, I'd like to consider myself a Christian, but I don't see what that has to do with church—any church! There's no club in the world easier to join than an American church, and no place I know where more absurd activities and more annoying people can get in between you and God. I've tried more churches than I'd care to name, and I've been treated to dismal sanctuaries, music that was either maudlin or unsingable, clergymen who were either errand boys and disrespected as such or pulpit prima donnas you could never get to know, indigestible casseroles at pointless church suppers, and that special blunt brand of rudeness of those who seen to hold title to the pews by some kind of traditional squatters' rights.

"I've found there's no fight quite as bitter as a church fight. There's no competition quite as self-defeating as competition among churches. And there's no membership in any other organization I know that seems to care less about what they stand for.

"Sure, sure, a man is some kind of an odd-ball today if he doesn't wish to God he had some religion. But that's an individual affair and all a church does for me is clutter it up. If it's your cup of tea, go on and enjoy it, because I suppose for those who are in the thick of it it can be fun, a pleasant sort of thing, a nice affair to belong to. That just hasn't been my experience."

Jack felt heat in his face that had nothing to do with the warmth of the morning. "Until your punch line I could have doubled every bid you made, but that climax fixed me. A pleasant activity! An enjoyable thing to belong to!

"Mister, a church is a frustrating thing to belong to, an exasperating thing to belong to, at times an infuriating thing to belong to, if you take it seriously. Don't you think those of us on the inside could give you a more complete indictment of any church's mistakes than any outsider ever could? Why the whole history of the church is a story of confusion, a crazy mixed-up compound of glory and shame, triumph and failure, loyalty to the best and treason against it. Because the real church—which a local church, most of the time, only points a finger toward—is nothing less than the laboratory of the new community of mankind which God's love through Christ keeps trying to shape humanity into. It is nothing less than the laboratory of a God-created community, called into this world by Him and depending on Him for all its life and energy.

"Little wonder it gets ugly! Little wonder for its greatness and its failures, because in spite of that magnificent origin and purpose, it's still made up of people like you and me, people exactly like you and me. And against the searchlight of what the church at its best ought to be, our lives aren't exactly pretty!

"The Christian church as you actually see it is a ship that's been sailing the seas of the years for quite a stretch now, and it keeps picking up a good many barnacles that veer it off course. Now and then it goes through storms that wash its equipment overboard. Is it surprising that from time to time it has to be taken into drydock to have the barnacles chipped off and the lost equipment restored and its original maps recharted so that the same ship can be launched on true course again? You don't have to give me a detailed inventory of the barnacles. I'll lay you odds that I could come up with a longer list than you can. And today it's hard to tell whether we're living through the drydock or the storm.

"No, I didn't come over to this bus stop to argue, either; but since it has come up, let's get it said. You talk about wishing you had a religion today. Well, why not? There are a dozen or so floating around, and those floating around are worth about a dime a dozen!

"If you had in mind the Christian religion, don't think you can brush off the church. The Christian religion just happens to require some church. There simply is no such thing as an individual, private Christianity. Some private cultivation and preening of your own soul in whatever homegrown hothouse you can afford may have a lot to say for itself—as long as it's clear to you that there is no such thing as private, individual Christianity. The only Christianity there has ever been requires a membership in and a concern with one of these laboratories of faith—barnacles and all, warts and all, failures and all! The church is the only organization on earth that requires as a prerequisite to our belonging to it the realization that none of us is ever going to deserve to belong, and yet must.

"William Temple put it unforgettably when he said that it is in the nature of the church, whatever it may be accomplishing at a given moment, always to seem to be failing. In any hour of history, look at Jesus Christ fairly and He will attract us; but look at His church and it will repel us by how far short it falls of its Lord.

"That's the paradox you've been glaring at across the street. It's as if with each generation, right in the teeth of whatever's threatening humanity the worst, the Master Conductor is calling together another ragtag orchestra of amateur musicians and asking us to play music that's so great we can't quite play it! Yet, in the very trying and for all our bungling, for all the discordant sound of our efforts, some things get done for God in our time. Some things get done for Christ that, without the church, wouldn't get done.

"Oh, here comes the Oakwood bus. You said you were taking this one, didn't you?"

The man answered, "Yes, I'd like to try taking the same bus you are."

But he was not looking toward the bus. He was staring across the street at the church.

6

On Being Stuck With Hell

The only inviting aspect of the barber shop was that you could see from the street that all three barber chairs were empty. Jack grinned inwardly at Jo's predictable reaction to his coming here again. He could hear her normally low voice go shrill with exasperation: "Jack, no! You didn't! I could do better than that barber with a home kit. What does he use, hedge clippers and a lamp shade?"

To be sure, there was no defending Pete's artistry as a barber, only his speed. Once over lightly, a few awakening scrapes from a sometimes sharp razor, two dabs on the neck with a styptic pencil, and you'd be on your way. And in a complex world there were times when any old haircut was considerably better than no haircut at all—a philosophy Jack wished his sons could come by, whether by contagion or transfusion.

Inside, the shop seemed too small for all those barber chairs. They rested, motionless, like three very ancient, chrome-headed monsters mummified in a black leather that seemed to have defied the centuries. A squat little electric clock behind the third chair chattered away in a throaty voice, as if it had some insistent message to give about the passage of time and was annoyed because no one could decode it.

Pete the barber gave Jack a rather restrained smile. Pete's greetings were always carefully graded according to tips and frequency of visits. This was not his full-dentured, "Welcome-again-old-regular" smile. This was his "Wonder-where-you-go-when-you-don't-come-here?" smile, and it required a bare minimum of facial rearrangement for the effort.

Pete managed to look like a veteran character actor who had once made up for a role as a barber and had been typecast ever since; tall and stooped, and beginning to bald, as befitted a man who did a fair side-business in hair-restorer, you couldn't imagine him without his barber's jacket. You got the notion that he ate in it, bathed in it, slept in it—that by now it had grown onto him.

Jack arranged his coat on a bent hanger, loosened his tie, and climbed aboard the indicated chair as one might mount a camel, bracing for Pete's inevitable question, "Been cold enough for you, Reverend?" The title was his own fault, Jack reflected. Long ago Pete had asked him, "Are you *Doctor* or *Reverend?*" As matter of factly as if he were asking, "Are you animal, vegetable, or mineral?" Resisting as too folksy the impulse to say, "Just call me Jack," he had lamely countered, "I'll answer to most anything." But he hadn't reckoned with a steady diet of "Reverend," which, as Pete slurred it, seemed a little south of "St. Jackson" and a little north of "Brother Wilson."

Pete's greeting seemed the signal for the newspaper that had been held motionless and unrustling over in the corner to be lowered, disclosing the occupant of the only easy chair in the shop. He was a thick pork chop of a man, looking rather too ruddy for that time of year, hair clipped close in a salt-and-pepper crew cut. His knit tie was twisted around till the bright red trademark showed and seemed to be tagging the man's generous stomach rather than the tie. There was a hard line to his jaw which belied the first-impression pudginess of his face as he took Jack in and asked tonelessly, "You a preacher?"

Jack closed his own jaw hard. What was there about February that kept you taut and edgy as a harpstring? "Yes, I am," he answered.

"Where's your church?"

Again Jack answered. The big man nodded, "Oh, yes, I know where that is," as if only on that basis could the information be true.

The newspaper was folded and tossed aside. "Well, I'm glad to meet you," which was an oddity because he didn't look glad about it at all. As a matter of record, no one had met anyone as yet, because you don't introduce yourself in barber shops any more than in elevators. But the man was growling on, "I've been wanting to ask one of you preachers for a long time—Whatever happened to hell?"

As he sighed, Jack hoped it wasn't audible above the buzz of Pete's No. 1 clippers. All he wanted was a haircut.

"I say—Whatever happened to hell?"

Jack managed to answer lightly, "Why, I suppose it's still there, wherever 'there' is. I haven't had word of any change in arrangements."

The stranger was not to be humored out of his cross-examination. He sat forward on the edge of the chair to say accusingly, "Now there's a vague answer, if I ever heard one. You preachers today don't sound much like preachers ought to sound. You won't answer a straight question. Reverend Whoever-You-Are, do you or do you not believe in hell?"

Pete had put away his clippers and was snipping slowly

with the scissors. Jack thought grimly, *The better to hear you with, my dear.* He hoped his neck did not look as red as it felt

"Look, Mr. Inquisition, if you knew me a lot better than you probably ever will, you'd find more and more ways that I fall short of even my own ideas of how a preacher ought to sound. You put your question in a way that suggests to me that you don't really know what you're asking. But here's as close as I can come to answering what you seem to think you're asking.

"Yes, I believe in God's judgment, both in this world and beyond it. Yes, I believe all our traditional notions of hell point to some terrible reality that is possible in whatever follows this life.

"Now I don't like to believe that. Show me a man who enjoys it, who really relishes believing that, and you'll probably show me a sick man. But as someone who is trying, however clumsily, to make sense of life through the eyes of Jesus Christ, I think that I'm stuck with believing it!"

The man's face had turned redder, and he sat back in the chair, so surprised at the turn the answer had taken that his expression was somewhere between a pout and a blank. "Stuck with it," he echoed. "Well, I never! You mean that you believe something you don't want to believe?"

Jack's sense of the ridiculous had muscled in to help by now, and his short laugh was honest. "Oh, yes. A good many things. I don't want to believe that I need forgiveness as often or as much as I happen to know I do. Because, you see, there is something about the Christian faith we constantly seem to be losing sight of today.

"There is such a thing as basic Christianity, which is what it is and was what it was long before you and I came along, and whether we like it or not. There isn't any one church, or any one tradition—certainly not any one mere man—which has ever had a corner on it, has ever been able to capsule it and hand it to you and me and say, 'Here it is; swallow this and you've got it!' But there's still such a thing as basic Christianity, and it isn't a supermarket where you can shop for beliefs that suit your fancy, telling the grocer, 'I'll take a dozen of these and a dozen of those, but none of this and none of that.' We have no such bargain-hunter's options.

"The Christian faith is a certain set of interlocking claims; it's a related family of ideas about who God is, and what is real, and how life works. Now, you can say it's all nonsense; you can bet the whole direction of your life that Jesus Christ is wrong—many have, many do.

"But if you're honestly trying to take Him seriously, then you're somewhat in the position of the lads who counsel with me now and then and tell me, 'Look, I want to marry this girl. But I want it understood that I'm not marrying her family. I like her father, but I don't care for her mother. I enjoy her aunt and uncle, but deliver me from her brother and those sisters!' So often I have to remind one of these young men, 'Don't fool yourself, son. If you marry this particular girl, you do marry this family. Because they're a close-knit clan. And though you needn't live with all of them all of the time, you're going to be stuck with some of them most of the time.'

"In all the family of Christian beliefs the ugliest and hardest-to-live-with member is this belief in some kind of judgment we call *hell.* But no matter how little family resemblance he carries and how often he seems at odds with all the rest, he's a close relative to all our other beliefs.

"Understand, I don't say we're stuck with any specific

notion of it, or description of it, or imagery about it. The diagrams and illustrations from Dante's *Inferno* have no more claim on our faith than the vulgar cartoons from the babblers of brimstone who have hurt this belief in its own house. I think we must even remember that Christ's own words about it were meant to be more pictorial than actual, to help us in our imaginations to see something we can't quite conceive. That's why He changed the pictures so often.

"By the way, it's a shocker to notice how often the so-called gentle Jesus did talk about hell—sometimes as a burning torment, but just as often as a sentence of exile, or a closed door you can't enter, or a welcome home you can't share; a being banished away from warmth and light; a cold, wandering, dark lostness. I doubt if much more is to be learned from Jesus' own word-pictures than from our puzzled acceptance of a dreadful possibility that's meant to seem terrible when thought about—and it's meant to be thought about.

"You see, if a game is played that's worth winning, it must be possible to lose that game, too; otherwise it's no true game, it's rigged. We believe life is worth living because it's a game worth winning; and the way it's lived has consequences. The direction we take has results, results that carry over and continue beyond the change of scenery we call *death.*

"Here's the way C. S. Lewis approached it a few years ago. I can't quote him exactly, but this is how he reasoned. Try to imagine a man who has made a career of treachery and cruelty, and has arrived at wealth and power by taking advantage of every decent trait of those he dealt with, even his family, even those who were once his friends. He has even sneered consistently at any goodness in his victims as so much spineless softheadedness. So he has crawled to his own apparent success over the broken hearts and lives and careers of others. Rather than mellowing, as we'd expect, he has silenced all pangs of remorse or conscience, and pictures himself as a model man who's been clever enough to outmaneuver God and the human race. He really enjoys, so far as he understands enjoyment, a good many years of the spendable dividends of ruthless self-centeredness. Then, with no change of heart whatsoever, he dies. Lewis's question is: What will you ask the God of justice, who really detests wrong, to do?

"Why, of course, it's an exaggerated picture! No, I've never personally known so monstrous a man, either. But that was done deliberately so that we wouldn't identify the description as anyone we know, because the moment you or I say of anyone we know, 'He deserves hell,' we're saying what no mortal dare say about another.

"But answer it—What would you ask God to do with such a man? Give him another chance? Why, God was trying to do that all the man's life, and he'd have none of it. Forgive him? Oh, God did that, from His side of things. But forgiveness is no blank check; it's a two-way traffic: it must be accepted as well as offered. This man refused to be forgiven. So what's God to do? Just go away and leave that man alone? You know, perhaps that's what He will do—just go away and leave the man all to himself. That just may be the hell of it! Forever and forever, with never, never an appeal from that sentence? I suspect that's a question we've never been equipped to ask or answer. I can imagine that Christ's comment might be, 'What's that to thee? Follow thou Me.' "

Jack was buttoning his coat and glancing in the mi
Really not too bad a job, considering what Pete had to
with. Jo couldn't complain too much this time. He paid
and nodded to both men and went out.

The man in the chair scratched his jaw and said, "
you are, Pete. Just the way I've told you. That's the wa
all are today. Never a straightforward answer to a
question. That's why I haven't been near a chur
twenty years." And he yawned and picked up his
again, and turned to the last page to read the obitua

7

The Problem of Mr. Wonderful

It hadn't always been easy to talk with, or as the hucksters of jargon would insist, "to communicate with," Jack, Jr. Of course, Jack reminded himself for perhaps the ten thousandth time, he, Jack, Sr., had never been a minister's son. He really had never known how much weight to give the popular assumption that a minister's children were under a different set of stresses in their most vulnerable years than, say, a lawyer's or a farmer's children.

Were they, really? Did they feel they lived in a goldfish bowl? Were they so defenseless, as many insisted, against the harpoons of self-appointed disciplinarians who, out to cut rather than cure, felt it their Christian duty to remind them at every childish breach of the community mores, "And you, a minister's son!"? Or was it that the clergyman and his wife were far more sensitive to this than the children themselves? Jack didn't know. And since Dr. Spock had never written so much as a small opus on "Little Talks With Clerics About Their Children," or "Sibling Rivalries Among P.K.'s," he had decided he probably never would know.

Bill and Joan, fifteen and thirteen respectively, certainly seemed to relish their roles. Jack had the notion that their status had made hams rather than hamsters out of them.

The problem with them was not one of communication, but of shifting their strident monologues to dialogues, and keeping them quiet long enough to listen to someone else!

Hadn't young Jack's teens been according to script for the nineteen sixties? His parents had endured the rock-'n-roll days with clenched teeth, along with other parents; now they felt much like the French priest who, when asked what he did during the French Revolution, answered, "I survived." They had known what a friend meant in his diagnosis of adolescence as "that disease which never kills the one who has it, only those who try to cure it." There were moments when they'd have agreed with another who insisted, "the only way to live with them is to lock them in a cellar with radio, TV, and record player, and every day or so toss a fishhead down to them, and not let them out till they're nineteen!"

Yet, looking across the room at this college freshman, Jack would have laid high odds that his son was going to be quite a man once he decided what to be a man about. He was well over six feet now—where did this generation get its size?—and dressed in the costume his peers demanded: shirt with shirttail out, sneakers on his feet and no socks, a pair of high-shinned khakis worn uncomfortably tight from waist to shank, and woefully needing a haircut. Jack wondered if any generation of city-bred Americans since the Civil War had so habitually needed haircuts. But his son's taut frame, more or less trussed up in this far-from-flattering garb, somehow hinted that it could, any day now, flesh out into a powerful musculature of maturity. That made it a pictograph of the person involved, this boy-man who might suddenly, in mind and spirit, flesh out into powerful sinews of selfhood.

To what purpose? For what issue? In which direction? God help us!—Was every year of our lives in its own way a crucial crossroad, if only we knew it?

All of which made these occasions as important as they were enjoyable, especially when young Jack volunteered such a discussion as that of the moment. He sat with his long fingers crossed and he slumped negligently in the chair but his always-dark eyes had their even darker focus of intense interest as he said, "Now remember, Dad, I'm not arguing with you; I'm asking what you think. That's a switch, isn't it? But this puzzles me more now than it ever did before.

"I guess that when you grow up in a church, as a kid you take it for granted that some people are wonderful and all that because they're good Christians; and other people are so-and-so's because, no matter what they say, they're not good Christians. That doesn't hold very long. Once you start mixing it up with all kinds of people, lots of them who haven't anything to do with any kind of church, you wake up to something. And I'll bet it bothers more young people than anything else about religion.

"All Christians aren't better people than all non-Christians! They just aren't! Some of the people I admire and enjoy the most have just missed all their Christian connections.

"No! Wait, Dad. I'm not arguing, remember? I've got someone very definite in mind. There's a college prof—and I won't tell you which one he is because I don't want you teeing off on him if you ever meet him—he's a tremendous guy, see? They call him brilliant, but that word's made of rubber, stretches into most any shape. What I know is, he's far too intelligent a man not to admit that there may be some kind of a God somewhere. He has told me that it's hard for him to look around the universe and fail to see some evidence of some kind of terrific Power and perhaps even a great Mind that's been at work behind that Power. But what he says is, if there is a personal God, then he for one, so far as he knows, has never had any sort of personal dealings with Him.

"So far as Christianity is concerned, he's respectful about it, courteous about it, willing for you and me to go in for it. But he wants no part of it. He apparently feels no need of it. Yet he happens to be a wonderful man. His family loves and admires him. His friends enjoy and trust him. His neighbors not only respect him, they depend on him for so many things. He seems to be making that kind of success I've heard you call 'the fine art of being alive.' But he is not a Christian! Yet so far as some of us can see, he's a much finer man than a good many, or a good many convinced Christians I could name for you right here in your church.

"How can that be, from a Christian point of view? How is it possible, Dad? That's what I'm asking."

Intrigued as he was with the head of steam Jacky had worked up in the presentation, Jack here and there had struggled to suppress a smile. He seemed to hear his own voice saying the same things not so long ago; at least it seemed not so long ago. Now he did smile and nod his head before he spoke. " 'The Problem of Mr. Wonderful'—I've thought about it so often I've given it a chapter heading in my own mind. And if he ever ceases being a problem to you, buddy, it will mean you've stopped thinking, or stopped trying to think, like a Christian.

"Of course I'm badgered by the little girl's complaint, 'Why can't Christianity make all the bad people good and all the good people nice?' Here's this Good News about God and life which we treasure. Why doesn't it improve the people who believe it more noticeably and more consistently? The only way I can ever steal a march on that puzzle is to realize that it isn't a question I'm in a position to ask.

"My question has to be—Why doesn't it make a far better man out of me than I am? Well, that one I can answer. The blunt truth is: I don't let it. I resist Christ in more ways than I'm ever aware of. I was born an incurable rebel against the love of God; and I'll be that, more or less, till the day I die. Which is just another way of saying that I belong to the human race.

"You see, Jacky, you've hit on a whole fistful of questions on your way around to your punch question. And I notice you're grinning because you know what a crank I am about trying to decide what it is that we're asking. There for a minute it seemed to boil down to a question: If Christianity is what it claims to be, then why aren't all Christians obviously finer, better, more contagiously enjoyable people than anyone else? That's a question that does manage to get itself asked. But it does not manage to get itself answered because, put in that way, it has no business ever being asked.

"What's wrong? Fall off around that curve? Well, look at it this way. Let's say we'd be the first to insist that unless Christianity makes a big difference in a man's life, then either Christ cannot deliver what He claims, or H. G. Wells was right when he hucked the whole affair, saying, 'This Galilean is too big for our small hearts.' But you and I must remember that it is never possible to look the world over and split the human race into two great groups, those who are Christians and those who are not, and then go to work to measure by some yardstick of behavior how much better the one group scores than the other.

"You can use something I've found so helpful that I think of it as the 'C. S. Lewis Law.' He pointed out that humanity is never on a given day composed of those two camps: full-fledged Christians as opposed to full-fledged non-Christians. At any hour you choose to count noses, if you knew enough to do the counting, you'd find many people who are falling away from Christianity, though they still think they're Christian; you'd also find many people in the process of becoming Christians, though they don't realize how close they are to it. You'd find many people who object to our theological claims about Christ, and our traditional creeds, but they admire Him so, and He is so real and attractive to them, that they are His far more than they could understand or we could explain.

"And you'd find people in other religions who, at that moment, are being led along some of God's secret corridors of the human heart to emphasize those points of their faith which Christ would approve. They are, as Paul put it, 'living according to what light they have,' and these are Christ's people without ever knowing it. And then you'd find legions of people who are simply muddled, who have a jumble of inconsistent and unexamined beliefs borrowed from every source imaginable, and who couldn't for the life of them tell you in which camp they belong. So there simply isn't any way you can take a behavior yardstick to Christians and non-Christians, because God alone knows which is which!

"Don't forget that, Jack. It's one of the trickiest mental traps we can fall into if we do. You just don't get anywhere by trying to compare 'Christians in general' with 'Non-Christians in general.'

"We get somewhere by keeping in mind someone we actually know. Take your Mr. Wonderful, for example, this great prof of yours, who is a fine man but not a Christian.

Now, careful here—we won't learn much by comparing him with, say, Mr. Ordinary who is a Christian and honestly is trying to be a truer one. But let's say we've found him not very wonderful, not too admirable, not so enjoyable. He has his points, Mr. Ordinary, but you have to catch him with his most genial foot forward; and we've caught him too many times and found him disappointingly ill-tempered and narrow-minded and powered by a hard-to-handle aggressive envy.

"Then there is his wife, Mrs. Ordinary, who tempts you to write her off as a thorough witch. She so enjoys saying things that hurt people. She's a character-assassin with that tongue of hers. Yet, if you knew her well, you'd discover to your amazement that she too is trying to be a Christian.

"What can you discover about the way Christianity works by comparing the enjoyable Mr. and Mrs. Wonderful, who have no discernible faith, with the exasperating Mr. and Mrs. Ordinary, who go in for faith? The truth is, Jacky, you can't learn much of anything that way. There is never much Christian wisdom to be gained by comparing one person with another quite different person. The wisdom comes when, in the light of what Christ offers to anyone, you compare a man with himself or a woman with herself.

"Sound absurd? Well, let's not lose each other on this one. It's too important. The Christian question never is, 'How can Jim Wonderful be so enjoyable with no known relation to Christ? Why can Jack Ordinary be so difficult when he professes Christ?' The Christian concern is, 'How much more magnificent a person could Jim Wonderful be if he became a Christian? How unbearable would Jack Ordinary be if he were not one?' Alice Wonderful is just naturally kind and thoughtful without an admitted faith; Betty Ordinary is such a trouble-maker in spite of her faith. The Christian concern is, 'What new strength of motive and staying power could come into Alice's kindness if she knew Christ? What kind of a deadly little cobra would Betty be if she paid no attention to Christ at all?'

"You see, if my doctor tells me I need to wear a certain kind of arch support, I have the right to expect that if I wear them my arches will improve. But if you should discover that I, who may have come by miserable arches from a long line of flat-footed Wilsons, even by wearing these supports do not have arches to compare with some young husky from the hills who seldom bothers to wear shoes, much less arch supports, you cannot on that evidence indict my doctor for inadequacy. The one situation would have nothing to do with the other; that mountaineer and I started life on such radically different feet!

"That's what God always remembers, but you and I seem artists at forgetting it. We all start life on such radically different feet. There's no such thing as a democracy of basic equipment. Countless natural causes, plus every pressure of environment, plus those hands from out of the past we call heredity, and all of it modified, here more and there less, by our own deliberate choices—all of this shapes the raw material of you into a different pattern from someone else.

"Here's a man who is a likable person, but it's quite possible that it is no credit to him. Factors he didn't summon have fitted together to turn him out in a pleasant dispositional pattern, just as so many factors fit together to produce a lovely landscape. Now, I happen to be able to imagine God enjoying a lovely landscape, but can you think He gives it much credit for arranging itself?

"Here's another man who has every right to be a terror, poisoned by a wretched inheritance or a childhood exposed to crippling passions and violence, nagged at daily by complexes that turn his best intentions inside out. We judge him by that other man; God doesn't. To whom much has been given, from him one whale of a lot is expected. I've cherished the remark of that tightly-wound executive whose mild-mannered associate chided him for his temper, and who answered evenly, 'I'm sorry, but do me the favor of remembering that I control more temper in fifteen minutes than a joy-boy like you feels in a lifetime!'

"Don't be surprised, Jacky, if you find a good many Mr. Ordinaries trying to keep company with Jesus Christ, a good many who can't point to much measurable fruit of the Christian spirit. For all you know, God's principal reaction to them is, 'Isn't it amazing they do as well as they do!'

"And don't be surprised to see a good many Mr. Wonderfuls who won't so much as look in Christ's direction. They see no reason why they should; and that's why they are in such danger, the danger of assuming that their personal enjoyability is a permanent thing and is all their own doing. They are in danger of crediting themselves with what's given them, as Mascagni once dedicated one of his operas 'To myself with affectionate esteem and unalterable satisfaction.' You see, the problem of Mr. Wonderful finally is: he's such a problem to God. Not only does he need to be saved from himself, just as much as Mr. Ordinary, but saving him happens to be tougher.

"God wants the same thing from every one of us, whatever our strengths or weaknesses, vices or virtues, whatever our native equipment. He doesn't want only obedience. Did it ever occur to you He could get that at a snap of His cosmic fingers, if that's all He were after? He doesn't want just a certain pattern of 'nice guy' behavior. Chew on this,

Jacky—if by some worldwide miracle we could wake up tomorrow morning and find the whole world peopled by 'nice guys' who felt no need of God, then this would for a while be a saner, safer, pleasanter world. But *Experiment Humanity* would be in as much jeopardy as it is now, from where God views it!

"God wants from each of us the free, unforced recognition and response to His love. God wants a man, whoever he is, to return to Him, to hand back his rebellious will to Him, as a son might in time recognize and respond to the forgiving love of the best of fathers.

"That's what it's all about, Jacky. God was in Christ to turn rebels into sons. It's too big to be glib about, but now and then it has to be summed up in some way. In view of what He's finally after, those words 'good,' 'bad,' 'nice,' 'fine,' become surprisingly petty and incidental, both in this life and through whatever other chapters of existence we might conceivably be processed to get His results.

"I'm glad you like your Mr. Wonderful. But you'll understand, I hope, if I'm not nearly so impressed by him as I am by the astounding fact that God has never lost His taste for 'bad' company."

Jacky sat silent a moment, then stood and walked to the door, turning to say without smiling, "I've changed my mind, Dad. If you ever do meet my friend, Mr. Wonderful, I won't mind your mixing it up with him at all. I believe you can hold your own."

Jack nodded and smiled but turned his head quickly till he was certain Jacky was gone. Fathers are big grown men. They're not supposed to get a hint of moisture in their eyes; at least, not from such faint praise. Why, that would embarrass any son!

8

The Work and the Weapons

It was late on a hot July afternoon when Jack saw the Red Telephone which in thirty seconds could plunge our country into irrevocable war, or unleash retaliatory powers beyond any nightmare or imagining. Jack was surprised to find it the same size as any other telephone. It only seemed larger, ominously larger than any telephone in the world, there on one corner of the General's desk, a solid dull red color oddly reminiscent of one of the less shocking shades of fingernail polish.

There was no dial on it, only a small red button where the dial should have been. Standing so close to it, Jack noticed that his friend from Chicago made a half-motion of his hand, as if to reach out and touch it in a childlike gesture of seeing if it were real. The Senior Control Officer on duty in the cubicle smiled understandingly, with no trace of disapproval.

He seemed young for a colonel and trim as any pilot, and he had an ease about him, even an unexpected kindliness toward such civilian gawking. But if you looked carefully, you could see faint lines of strain written in indelible shorthand on his face. Something deep in his eyes hinted that his relaxed manner was as practiced and official as his uniform, something to be put on or taken off as the moment required.

Offutt Air Base, a few miles south of the stockyards of Omaha, Nebraska, seemed on the ground not drastically changed from the last time Jack had seen it some fifteen years before. Oh, you did notice how much longer the airstrips were, explained by huge yellow signs out on the highway advising motorists not to be alarmed by the noise of jet engines. And you did notice clusters of new buildings, and a stark, full-sized model of an Atlas missile near headquarters. It was a sharp finger pointing up as a cathedral might point. But this finger was pointing not in praise; it was a threat, a reminder, a warning.

The skin-prickling impressiveness of Offutt Air Base in this year of our Lord was not on the field. It was underground, far underground, down in "The Hole," as the Air Force had bluntly christened it. Down there is both the beating heart and the brain of America's Strategic Air Command. Down there is a world and a plan that could not possibly be, yet is.

Three stories down you walk, after you've been cleared, down long ramps past three checkpoints of eight-inch steel doors, along massive corridors of concrete flanked by armed guards wearing blue berets and looking astonishingly young, like boys playing soldier, until you notice their expressions. Then you know they aren't playing. You finally stand before a television camera that flashes your picture back to all the security officers you've passed, as a final check on your clearance. Then you step, blinking, into the bright but noticeably shadowless artificial light of The Hole.

For a moment, what you see is meaningless; all you feel is bewilderment at this polished, alien, self-contained little universe with fifty feet of solid concrete and steel above your head.

The great war room is so designed that the General's command post is an elevated, glass-enclosed balcony from which he can watch all activity on the floor and have an unobstructed view of the many panels on the map wall which is some twenty-five feet high and perhaps three hundred feet long. The world is on those maps, and the shifting weather of the world, and the changing location of our every bomber squadron.

A great row of clocks hung from the ceiling show at a glance what time it is in every major capital. One clock is painted red and shows zero time; it will start ticking only if and when.

To the left of the control cubicle the wall panels of the great room are covered with large squares of opaque green plastic. These panels you do not see, for on them is mapped the complete plan of battle.

Inside the command post one closed-circuit TV screen is open day and night on another command post in Denver, SAC's alternate brain. Another TV screen shows constantly-mapped reports on any unidentified flying objects in our radar hemisphere. It was all explained to Jack with such disarming matter-of-factness that the full import of what they were saying bored into his comprehension slowly with a series of delayed shocks. If we have thirty minutes' warning, we win! If we have twenty minutes' warning, we are terribly hurt but we still win. If we have any minutes' warning, though the odds are conclusive that no one wins there still can be put into motion immeasurable retaliatory havoc and destruction for the enemy.

On the Commanding General's desk there are actually

four telephones. One is a direct line to the White House; one is a direct line to the Pentagon; one is an alternate line to the red telephone. By law the President or his surviving successor "owns" all nuclear bombs and missile warheads; the Commanding General of SAC has only the custody of them. Permission to release them would take, at most, ninety seconds—if there is a White House, if there is a Pentagon; if not, it must be the Commanding General of SAC's decision. That is why, of the four generals sharing this command, at no time of the day or the night can any of them be farther than twenty tested minutes away from that glass cubicle unless they are on leave.

By lifting the red telephone and pressing the red button the Commanding General would instantaneously speak to our bases all over the world through loudspeakers always tuned in. In thirty seconds the first bombers could take off to join those already in the air around the clock; the others would follow in a matter of minutes. They all must await the second message, "Proceed to target." That would be it. That would start the countdown on every missile we have aimed. That would send over three hundred bomber crews, each jet-streaking at a particular target, long memorized, so often drilled and rehearsed that the navigators would need no maps.

In a daze, Jack found his voice husky as he thanked the Control Officer for his time. He noticed that the officer's smile was not mechanical; it was human and it was tired. He wondered what kind of life this would be to be sentenced to, this constant vigil no mortal is built to maintain.

Jack went back up the ramps slowly, passed the checkpoints, and back out under the Nebraska sunshine on the flat field so near the river it would have done well planted in corn rather than concrete. A steak dinner at the Officers' Club was welcome but tasteless for all its excellence.

He knew that all he was thinking and feeling he would not be able to catalogue later for total recall. And as he caught sight of the official seal of the Strategic Air Command, enlarged and framed on the wall, he wondered which was saner, to laugh at the irony of it or wink back tears at the hope of it. For the seal is a great clinched fist with jagged lightning flashing from it, and the fist is holding—an olive branch! The slogan is, "Peace Is Our Profession"!

The drive back from the air base seemed longer than the drive out had been. None of the men in the cab had much to say above the changing whine of the gears and the whir of tires and the pattern of traffic noises. Even the ticking of the taxicab meter occasionally made itself heard. Then one of the men, a wiry, tightly coiled little man from Chicago, said to no one in particular, "I knew it had gone far but—great God in heaven!—has it gone this far? Is this kind of hammer already cocked on the twentieth century, needing so little to trigger it? Are we to live out our days under so constant a threat of destruction that all our tomorrows hang on whether we get twenty or thirty minutes' warning? Can you blame people for feeling helpless, knowing what all this can mean, yet watching the nations stumbling toward it like men caught in some blind hypnosis? Can you blame people for despairing at the bleakness of such a future?"

The man sitting beside Jack—a man whose knowledge and feeling for the artery of what being a Christian is all about Jack had learned to treasure these past few days—this man answered the other: "No, Joe, I can't blame people for despairing, but I can certainly blame myself. As a Christian I am sitting here pretty annoyed at myself. Of course it's a jolt to be forced to see what a cliff-hanger our day has turned into. Of course it's dazing and depressing to think how much of our planning is in terms of bare survival at a minimum cost of destroying half the world. But Nietzsche said somewhere, 'Don't stare too long into a dark abyss, or the dark abyss will stare back into you.'

"That's what we did, you know, down in The Hole. We preoccupied ourselves with one fiercely dark, dramatic set of facts."

He went on, his voice rising as if he felt he had held back long enough, "I'm wondering how long it is going to take my mind to muscle in on my mood with the fact that I'm supposed to be a Christian. I'm wondering how long it will take for quite another set of facts to reassert themselves in my thinking, facts every bit as real as the Red Telephone.

"One obvious fact is that in this threat of destruction for you and me, or yours and mine, we face nothing more than every human being who ever lived always faced. Wider spread, yes. More appalling as a global disaster, yes. But so far as men, one at a time, are concerned, it's the same old riddle man has faced since first he climbed up out of his cave and wondered about the meaning of it all. We each, in time, owe God a death, however it may come.

"As for the world, even that wonderful part of it we love and enjoy so—whether or not it should explode like some 50-watt lightbulb tomorrow, or whether it will churn on its way for millions of years, at last to be charred to a cinder or frozen to an iceball, the problem's the same. Everything that has ever happened, or ever will happen, depends for its final meaning on who God is. Who is this who sits above the circle of the earth, before whom its inhabitants are as the locusts, its nations only waves on time's ocean, and its rulers as nothing?

"Joe, when I decided to bet my life that God is exactly like Jesus Christ, I wasn't betting that all my questions could be answered, or all my doubts dispelled, or all the mysteries cleared away, or all suffering explained, or all trouble solved, or all dangers squelched. What I was betting my life on is that He is more interested in what finally becomes of you and me than we puny things could possibly be.

"He doesn't hang back in some eternal tomorrow to show that interest. Right here, right now, He is determined to rescue us if He possibly can. Wherever He can, without making puppets of us, our God is determined to rescue. That's why He has tricks with human history up His sleeve which make God's hands so much quicker than our eyes. That's why He turns up in the least likely hours, at the most unexpected times, and somehow uses even the worst man can do to His own advantage.

"That's why I must never despair of the hour in which I live. I can't possibly know what surprising use He may be about to make or even the threats of that hour just around the next corner. It isn't my job to know. My job is to get on with the work of trying to be a Christian in a non-Christian world, the work of trying to muster enough excellence and salvage enough mistakes and look at enough men through the eyes of a brother to demonstrate the livability of a life in praise of God right here in the twentieth century."

And suddenly Jack was aware that the taxi had stopped at the hotel entrance, and even the cabbie was listening, and the meter was still ticking. But no one seemed to mind.

There was even something reassuring in that odd little clock ticking away.

Halfway across the hotel lobby Jack realized that the Red Telephone was still hauntingly, menacingly real, but it seemed to have taken its place in a total picture. You still hated the very thought of it, but you remembered a day in ancient Jerusalem when some work was going on under constant threat of attack. It is written that those who carried burdens were laden in such a manner that each with one hand labored on the work and with the other held a weapon; and each of the builders had his sword girded at his side while he built. It was clumsy going, slow going, terribly dangerous going, but the work went on, the work on the walls of the City of God.

9

The Gospel Along Route 11

It seemed to come upon both men at the same time that they had been driving for too long in what had become an awkward silence. Not that silence itself was necessarily awkward between them; their friendship was close enough to afford times of silence. They had known each other long enough and well enough not to feel compelled to make small talk, to keep skirmishing around in the nervous little chatter of counterfeit conversation. Had it not been for what had happened miles back at the service station, neither would have felt any weight in this silence.

Both of them knew that Jack Wilson loved to drive, aware as he was of the murderous menace of an American highway today. Still, when traffic was light and it was a fair day and a good highway, when the car was running at its seasoned best and there was no tight schedule of arrival to shoot for, he simply loved to drive. He often said it was only because there was no telephone in the car; but his enjoyment had more ingredients than that. You'd have had to list a nonmechanically-minded man's enjoyment of handling machinery, and the feeling he'd confess to that when all was well the car seemed like some sort of extension of himself, from the power snoring evenly from under the hood to the undeviating purr of the tires on the highway. Jack even enjoyed the untaxing game of keeping that speedometer a hair under the posted limit, and scowling in the best tourist style of indignation at the monstrous trucks which roared past him at an easy eighty.

What's more, both men loved the Shenandoah Valley of Virginia, and since it was not their home they always had eyes to see it. They were just south of Winchester, where Route 11 flattens and straightens out and off to the left the foothills of the Blue Ridge begin. It was quite early in autumn, and green was still the prevailing color, yet any woodland stretch was strident with the unbelievable reds of maple and the more conservative reds of dogwood blowing like trumpets among the yellow trees and pedestrian rust of the oaks. It was a view both men normally would have enjoyed in silence, because it may well be that men enjoy beauty every bit as much as women do. But in today's male code the rule is rigorous: if you enjoy it, you must not exclaim about it!

Jack knew his passenger's quiet was a signal of a session of thought, not a mood of pout or withdrawal. The Reverend Dr. James McIver was a big man, big in body and mind and sensitivity, and possessed of the ability, rare in men as large as he, to make himself comfortable wherever he was, whether in the front seat of a car, or in the saddle of the horse he rode for diversion, or in his study with the German of Luther or the Latin of Tertullian. Jack was greatly relieved when, in that deep voice which was wired for volume from a pulpit but in conversation was surprisingly gentle, big Jim McIver, without turning his head, said quietly, "You were a little rough on the little man back at the service station, Jackson." Jack knew he had been waiting for some such comment.

It had been during a routine fuel check that the man back

at the service station had noticed the split in the fan belt. He had called Jack's attention to it, and with the impassive face that was a standard mask for all out-of-state customers, had said, "You'd better let me change this fan belt, mister. It's split nearly through. May go the rest of the day but could snap the next mile." Which was fine. Jack was grateful it had been noticed, until some thirty minutes later when the attendant motioned to him at the Coke machine.

From his tugging under the hood, beads of sweat stood out on the man's face, for all the comfortably cool morning. His hands were engine-grimed and his dark blue shirt was wet along the curve of his thin chest and the ridge of his shoulders. All formalities were dropped in his exasperation. "Buddy, do you know how this fool thing comes off? I've never changed one on this model, and I can't figure how you slip it off to slip the new one on."

Jack was sure it had been his own ignorance that had quick-fused him to bark, "Well, why didn't you tell me that before? If you don't know how to do it, why did you suggest that you take on something that's too much for you to handle?" Needled by that, the little man had crossed the street to a competitor whose mechanic handled it quickly. And the look of chagrin on the attendant's face hadn't noticeably eased even after Jack's more-than-customary tip.

Now, rolling along Route 11 past the fanfare of red maples, Jack admitted to Jim McIver, "I've felt foolish about it ever since, Jim, losing my temper and lipping off over such a little thing."

Big Jim shifted his considerable bulk and moved one great arm till it dangled down behind the front seat. "Knock off that part of it, Jackson," he growled, "I've no more use for a preacher without a temper than for a knife blade in the same sad shape. I wish more of us lipped off, as you put it, oftener—that is, if we knew more than we do, and our timing could be better than it is.

"What I'm saying is, you clobbered that little man back there for a reason that you and I, of all people, dare not clobber anyone. Remember what you said to him? I haven't been able to forget it. This foliage, these mountains, this valley won't take the edge off it. You said, 'Why do you take on something that's too much for you to handle?' Jack, if that question has any validity, then the whole human race had better close shop at five sharp this afternoon. Matter of fact, we're long overdue. Because this happens to be true of every one of us, every mother's son of us! This happens to be true of every mortal who's trying to make any kind of a fist today of the business of being alive. He doesn't know quite what to do about it, but sure as he's born, he has taken on something that's too much for him to handle!

"Jack, you know it as well as I do—we spend most of our time with all kinds of people. I don't know when it began to happen to us all. I just know that it has happened to us, and most of us know it. History is my hobby. You could say it's my escape. I know how silly it is for us to whine that we have it any worse than any other age, when in so many, many ways we have it so much better. But this is different. This, I'm convinced, is vintage twentieth century. I don't know of a time when as many people felt inadequate, incapable of facing and doing what they know they have to face and do—like your little man back there who found he'd taken on something that was too much for him to handle. Every other man I meet seems to have the look of it on his face, the slump of it in his shoulders when he doesn't know he's being watched; somewhere in his mannerisms there's some gesture of defeat. It's my daughter's phrase, but it says it—the twentieth century has done a snow job on us! And I tell you, our Lord didn't mean for us to feel so helpless and so hangdog and so futile—not the One who said, 'I came to bring them to life.' "

"Then what is the gospel on it, doctor? What is the Good News?" Jack asked it not as a jab but as if he were asking himself, too.

Big Jim took it at face value. "Why, doctor, the gospel on it begins with some new realization of that tremendous oversimplification that whatever more the cross of Jesus Christ is—and you know how much more I believe it is—at its simplest the cross is a plus sign.

"It means my pygmy strength plus the limitless power of God. It means my puny wits plus the immeasurable wisdom and resourcefulness of God. It means my fitful, scrambling attempts to love and forgive and believe and hope plus His outmaneuvering love and stubborn belief in me and endless hope for me. It means that anytime I'm trying to do the right thing or be the right person, as He has given me some glimpses of what the right is, I have going for me my own little efforts plus the good God Almighty. There's nothing new about that idea. But there would be something excitingly new in our really believing it today; if we the beaten, we the futile, we the snowed believed that in His plus is our only peace!

"No, keep your eye on the road, Jack. Just because we're slowing down and pulling into town, don't be glancing at me out of the corner of your eye to read some hidden nuance of meaning from my expression. I have never been able to do much about the look on my face, but I assure you I'm not playing with any hidden subtleties here.

"It's just that the deluge of whipped and cornered people I've met of late has set me back on my heels. That's an exercise which is good for clergymen, I'm told, but I don't recommend it for the area of fun and games. It's brought me to the realization that all of us give lip service to, but seldom really and honestly mean: anytime you take the bit of life in your teeth and try to go it alone, all on your own, you've a date up ahead with nothing but exhaustion, and sooner than later. I came to Christianity through a maze of alternatives, for what I was convinced at the time were solid intellectual reasons. And I still believe they hold good.

"But Jack, if they didn't, if they didn't quite hold good, I believe I'd go right ahead throwing myself on this gospel of Christ today, because without it, all we've got is paralysis—paralysis of any hope and courage, paralysis of any confidence in mankind's future, paralysis of any sense of an outgoing meaning to life.

"I don't know—and I haven't met anyone who claims he knows—what kind of corner our world is turning right now. I just believe that I'm not turning it alone, that God has His plans and His reasons and His own way of making human history finally make sense. And He's so amazingly generous that, after the hard time I've given Him all my life, I'm still a part of His plans—because in His plus is our peace."

They were quiet again as Jack flicked the turn signal and pulled the car over to the curb. For the first time in a good many miles he looked Jim McIver in the face. "We'd better get some lunch, Jim. And by the way, preacher, thanks for the sermon."

Jim fairly growled, but left a grin behind, "That wasn't a sermon, preacher; that was a confession. Or could it be that they always amount to the same thing?"

10

Realized Forgiveness

The Sunday morning services were over. Jack realized that he had stayed longer than usual at the church door, visiting with the few still lingering in the narthex. As he finally turned away he noticed that the lights in the sanctuary already had been turned off. He smiled to himself; the trustees would be pleased.

He walked back through the sanctuary up the center aisle, sensing the strange aliveness of an empty church just after worship. It seemed deserted but it felt far from deserted. How was it Carlyle Marney had said it? Somewhere, sometime, Jack had heard him say that it is a churchman's dream that of a Monday, when the custodians sweep out the sanctuary from Sunday's service, instead of umbrellas and odd gloves and idly penciled notes and discarded orders of service, here and there they might come upon such things as some big man's deep grief or another's disappointment or another's sense of failure; such things as some quiet woman's bitter hurt or another's painful pride or another's quarrel with God. Perhaps, far over in another section, so small you must sweep carefully to find it, might be some youngster's sin; whether real or imagined, it doesn't matter, so long as it was discarded. And here and there the far more bulky trash of a badly bruised ego, left behind where it belonged. All of this, in such a dream, was to be swept out and thrown away when church was over.

Jack had reached the front of the church and on unplanned impulse he walked up the carpeted steps into the chancel and sat at one of the prayer desks where he could turn and look back over the sanctuary. Marney was right—that should be any churchman's dream; that should be the kind of thing that can happen to people in church on any given Sunday, even though it doesn't happen to enough of us often enough. *Realized forgiveness*—Jack whispered the phrase audibly, as he often did when an idea struck him with new force—that's surely one of the indispensables in keeping Christianity going.

He doubted if there was much to be learned by sniffing back up the trail of our American church history, trying to spot where and when and why we began to be taken in by "Little Bo-Peep's mistake." Even though Little Bo-Peep didn't know where in the world to find her lost sheep, that didn't really seem to disturb her. "Leave them alone and they'll come home, wagging their tails behind them," was her formula.

Jack shook his head. Perhaps that worked with sheep but it didn't quite work with people. We mortals are strange creatures who cannot come home to life until we've learned how to be at home with God. Leave us alone and we can't come home, because of all these things we keep dragging behind us, even when we come to church.

Oh, not that we should try to avoid dragging our burdens with us on our way to worship. We couldn't keep from bringing them with us, even if we tried. All our unhealed quarrels and grooved grudges and unadmitted fears and chronic complaints and unresolved doubts and merciless attitudes come with us. But the hurt of empty worship is that while we are in church we can stay so preoccupied with all the rattling, noisy things we've trailed in through the doors that there's no real expectation of, no honest paying attention to, no eager waiting for some encounter with the God who can teach us how to leave some of this load of ourselves here when we go out. And when the service is over, and the organ sounds its grand postlude, and the preacher crawls down from an altitude he reached only in his own imagination, we get up and stagger out, dragging away the same junk we brought in with us.

Jack found himself staring up at the pulpit from which he had been preaching such a short time ago. We in the pulpit, he thought, though we can't tell exactly when it started, have been accomplices in the plot against realized forgiveness. It was with acid instead of ink that wonderful Phyllis McGinley wrote on the slick pages of *The New Yorker* an epitaph for a whole generation in her gem, "Community Church":

The Reverend Dr. Harcourt, folks agree,
  Nodding their heads in solid satisfaction,
Is just the man for this community.
  Tall, young, urbane, but capable of action,
He pleases where he serves. He marshals out
  The younger crowd, lacks trace of clerical unction,
Cheers the Kiwanis and the Eagle Scout,
  Is popular at every public function,

And in the pulpit eloquently speaks
  On divers matters with both wit and clarity:
Art, Education, God, the Early Greeks,

Psychiatry, Saint Paul, true Christian charity,
Vestry repairs that shortly must begin—
All things but Sin. He seldom mentions Sin.

Well, who could be found who would speak in defense of the Reverend Dr. Harcourt today, so recognizable in those barbed lines as the typical face of American Protestantism during certain years most of us here have lived through? In a way he seems to belong to so long ago, almost to belong to another world, this earnest, kindly, cultured, bouncy, optimistic, reassuring, but shallow, superficial, and tragically irrelevant young man who was the creation of his times rather than of his New Testament, and therefore seldom mentioned sin. Yet, as a matter of record, he flourished not long ago at all, in those strange years between the two great wars. And if no one is to be found today to speak in his defense, surely someone should be found to speak of him with understanding.

He hadn't read his Bible aright! But most of us hadn't. He had misread life! But most of us had. He was fooled! Most of us were fooled. For those were years when God's offer of forgiveness through Jesus Christ seemed dated and pointless and done for, when congregations of the faithful seemed to be yawning in the face of it. It was the answer to a question no one seemed to be asking, and people were saying, "Forgiveness? For what? Oh, I know I have some faults that need correction, some immaturities that need to be seasoned. I have some lack of knowledge that needs instruction and quite possibly a tinge of selfishness that needs redirection. But these are all good, normal, healthy faults. I certainly don't know of a thing about me that I need to be ashamed of."

And we thought they meant it; but we were wrong, for

they were wrong. We thought the very word *sin* was no longer usable, and so misused as to be worn out. It had been scorched, beyond any modern recognition, along too many sawdust trails. It had been mouthed by too many pale clerics. It had been spewed by too many cranks over every harmless enjoyment they happened not to enjoy. Jack had been only a year out of seminary when the attractive woman in her middle years had jolted him so forcefully he still could remember the lonely hurt in her eyes and the steady bitterness in her voice when she said, "Religion! No, thank you! So far as I can see, the emptiness of my whole life is that it hasn't had enough of what you sputtering preachers call sin!"

So most of us had thought, Why sputter? If the very term *sin* is unsalvageable, let's learn to talk of maladjustments and tensions and communication failures and lack of involvement and guilt complexes and inherited tendencies, for life has tossed sin out the window. We didn't know what was about to come bubbling up from the drain.

We didn't know that in our Anglo-Saxon tongue "hallowed be Thy name" and "Heil Hitler" could have the same roots. We didn't know there could be human roasting ovens and quick-lime pits and mass graves in Poland and Panzer divisions cutting like razors across the throat of mankind. We didn't know what a chaplain would see at Iwo Jima—and though he'll talk to his family about anything else in this world, to this day he'll talk to no one about that. We didn't know we could plaster a picture of a pinup girl on the incredible bomb that seared the life from Hiroshima.

We didn't know about the blood with which we'd irrigate Korea, or that behind the mushroom clouds of our new power to destroy would rise a red Kremlin like a grinning skull of doom, like sick religion's revenge for having been so long neglected. We didn't know that the explosion potential of China's fantastic population could ever threaten to engulf all Asia with a Marxism filtered through almond eyes turned cold and merciless. We didn't know yellow could ever mean red. We didn't know the mountain of Tibet could ever come to Mohammed. We didn't know the peace-loving Buddha could ever spawn the shock troops of human torches. We didn't know we'd ever see the day when the confident American of the easygoing conscience would talk wearily of our loss of national purpose and national integrity, and informed men could argue heatedly the timetables as to whether we'd reach the stars or destroy the world first.

We didn't know the little island of Cuba in our backyard could be turned overnight into an arsenal aimed at our head. We didn't know a President could be assassinated today, and with a sequel so sick the world would stare in disbelief at what could happen in America. We didn't know the Civil War wasn't over, not even in the North and East, and not in our hearts. We didn't know that this business of racial and color difference is so deep in the primitive core of man's self-centeredness that you can't touch it by some sudden rush of sweet reasonableness; and heaven help you if you're so naïve as to expect to, because you cannot possibly predict the panic of the reaction among the most sophisticated of us when that primitive core is threatened! We didn't know. We didn't know.

But—God forgive us!—we know now, don't we? We know now that we're not some special edition of the human story. There was never anything very special about us. We were and we are the same old story. We belong to the hell-tormented, heaven-storming generations of all mankind, and the chaos we decry is at work within us. The havoc we deplore around us is native to us. And we're all guilty. We're all guilty, whether it's big or little, global or local, whether it's the trucks that so long have rolled our highways under the tyranny of a brass-knuckled hoodlum or the new mood in American politics which no longer says, "I disagree with you," but howls, "If you disagree with me you're a traitor and no American!" Whether it's the drag race on the highway that mangles a child or the chilling surge of violence along our streets at night, it's all a vast and writhing projection of the mighty contradiction in which we're caught—that the good we want to do is so often what we won't do, and the wrong we despise is so often exactly what we will do! And that is sin. And my sin and your sin is our personal burden of the total gone-wrongness of life.

It doesn't help much to play mental parlor games of trying to untangle the strands of that knotted mass of yarn, to say, "Well, that went wrong because we didn't know better; and that and that and that went wrong because of circumstances so weighted in the wrong direction that the drift was too strong for us to change it; and only here and here and here are we really at fault." Sorting the bundle doesn't make the weight of it any lighter. Our sin is our personal burden of the gone-wrongness of life.

For those of us who are at last convinced that we can't run from it or hide it, that there's no point in denying it and yet some kind of high treason involved in despairing of it, the old, old words ring with more meaning in these days of our years than ever before in our lives. Our only hope, our only help lies in paying attention to God, the God who loves us not because we deserve it or earn it, but because we're His! He is the God of the Galilean face and voice, the

God with the scars, the God of the detective story Dorothy Sayers didn't try to explain; she just pointed at the cross and said, "For whatever reasons God made us as we are, limited and perverse and prone to pain, at least He had the honesty and the integrity to take His own medicine!"

So time circles round in history's loud, jangling carousel, and again the brass ring is crisis. So once again in this year of our Lord, when so many things make no sense at all, it makes good sense for a churchman to dream that of a Monday morning the custodians will sweep out with the junk some useless things someone discarded in church because some hint of the love of God enabled him to forget himself, and unload some of himself, and go out of church freer for a few days. Perhaps, because he had realized forgiveness, he was freer to prove the livability of the forgiven life.

11

But How Will They Know It's Easter?

Larry straddled a straight chair, both arms on the back under his chin. Jack slumped back on one elbow on the sofa in the corner of his study, taking a long last swallow from a bottle of Coke. Both men had unbuttoned their collars and loosened their ties. The Good Friday service always spent a man, not only by its length, but by its emotional intensity. Stofer's music had never been more exciting. Jack and Larry were tired, but in the way they liked being tired. They were glad to be left alone; people had a way of seeing to it that they were seldom left alone.

Larry spoke slowly, in that surprisingly deep voice. In appearance he was all boy; when he spoke he was all man. "Jack, Sunday will be my first Easter out of seminary, my first Easter here on your staff. It's strange—I'm both excited to see it come, and I dread to see it come. How do we keep from letting them down, Jack—all those people who crowd the church on Easter? So many of them with such vague notions of what it is we'll be celebrating. How do we make it real to them, Jack? They'll know they've been to church, but how will they know it's Easter?"

Jack sat up, placed the Coke bottle on the floor, and grinned at his assistant. "You always have the instinct for the artery, Larry. I get so teed off at the omniscient clerical pups who resent the crowds on Easter Sunday, as if somehow people cluttered the whole thing up just by being in church.

"Yours is the real question. Knowing this is one Sunday when they will be in church, how do we keep from letting them down?

"Ed Sutton will be here. How will he know it's Easter? I was over at his house, Larry. We sat for far too long before the fire in the living room. It wasn't really the warmth of the fire he wanted—it wasn't really cold in the house. I knew he wanted the near-hypnotic comfort of staring at logs blazing in a fireplace; and those watching don't need to say much, for so many things seem to get said without words.

"But when he suggested a cup of coffee in the breakfast room, I was all for it. I think he braced himself to face the breakfast room; it was so bright and cheerful. He spilled a little instant coffee on the shelf, and didn't wipe it off at once, the way she would have had she still been there. As he snapped on the lamp above the breakfast nook, I was afraid he would burn himself with the steaming kettle he held in the other hand. For he stared at the lamp for a moment, then reached up deliberately and snapped it off again, and said, as much for his own hearing as for mine, 'My faith is that it wouldn't make sense. It simply wouldn't make sense for her to go out, just to be turned off like that!'

"Larry, I doubt if you or I would ever be able to improve on what Ed was saying there as a summary of strictly human reasoning about life after death. Oh, it can be put in a thousand other sets and shapes of words. But I doubt if, on our own, we'd come up with any reasoning that goes far beyond what that terribly lonely man said there in his breakfast room. You see he was, for that moment, all humanity that has watched death as long as there has been life, and has known that 'We've each a darkening hill to climb,' and yet has defiantly said into the blank face of the unknown, 'No, it wouldn't make sense for whatever power pulled off this miracle of bringing us out of the dark to turn out our lights and plunge us back into the dark again.'

"It wouldn't make sense for death to be what it seems to be, the cold incoming tide that washes into pitiful little nothings all the brave sand-castles we've built on the beaches of our human yearning and dreaming and hoping. Whatever may be wrong with this life—and any day is a guided tour to how much is wrong with it—everything that's right about it feels like a promise of some life beyond it. Unless you and I spend our days deliberately living as if this couldn't possibly be so, we'll find we come equipped with a built-in inclination to expect life to have a sequel, some kind of great *to-be-continued.*

"So our Easter morning marching-order is not to quote sonnets about the springtime or to buff a new polish on old arguments. It is to see that the things we already desperately yet shyly want to believe about immortality come into focus—not just as a grand perhaps, but as a faith in the light of the Easter announcement.

"And let's call it the Easter announcement, Larry, not the Easter argument. If people could only see that the Christian church refuses to try to explain the resurrection, because it takes the resurrection to explain the Christian church! Nothing else could have shocked the church into existence. It took this, which, if you disconnect it from everything else that goes with it, will seem as fantastic today as it did to those two thousand years ago who laughed their pagan heads off at those credulous Christians. That story of theirs, that one morning at dawn two women went out to a tomb in a garden, not even noticing the dawning because to them the sun had gone down to stay. They didn't bring much; there isn't much you can bring to a tomb, except the ache-numbed steps with which they walked and the pain-drained memories they shared as they huddled together against the burdened sighing of the morning wind through the sycamore trees. But they met Someone at that graveside that morning, and nothing has ever been quite the same since. For then two men came racing, racing at that rumor of an empty grave, sounding staccato words to each other above the thud of their sandals on the cobbles of the dawn-streaked streets. Of course they couldn't believe the word the hysterical women had brought them! Who could? But they met Someone, too, and nothing has ever been quite the same since.

"But you know how the world works, Larry. You know that kind of report could never get a hearing, even if that appearance happened to others. The world doesn't swallow that kind of talk from anybody. And those were all decidedly nobodies—fishermen, peasants, villagers, housewives—hiding out from the police in the back alleys of a rundown province in the backwoods of a tottering empire. Their story would never even be heard, and if heard as promptly forgotten, for our world has always had brainwashing methods all its own.

"But the story was heard; it was not forgotten. The Easter announcement, with all the freshness of dawn still on it, tells us that Someone has done the impossible, has come back to tell us, has stepped through the curtain and then back into this room again to let us know, has walked through whatever gate a grave is and let the door close and the lock click behind Him—and then has come back out again so we could see.

"That was the announcement. It was not Christmas that up-ended the thrones of the Caesars. It was not the Sermon on the Mount. It was not the Parable of the Prodigal or any of the miracles of healing. It wasn't even the harshness of His cross. It was the resurrection of Jesus Christ that launched Christianity on the world and became the rock on which the church was built and has stood through whatever storms. This was the news release which God only knows how many million times since has dried the tears of the desolate and persuaded broken hearts to sing again. This it is that will bring us together in crowds in churches on Easter morning.

"And, thank God, the crowds will come, Larry! They can't know how welcome they are! Because the people are the excitement in the modern celebration of Easter. Take hold of that idea by both lapels, Larry. The continuing excitement is to be looked for not just up there in the choir loft or in the lectern with us or in the pulpit. There's no other Sunday of the year when so many people could be as certain of what we up there will sing or say. The real drama is out in the congregation where their very presence gives the lie to the modern pose of nonchalance before the riddle of death.

"Think how many varieties of belief as to the possibility of personal permanence will be in our congregation this Sunday. How many practical Thoreaus will be present, cautious even about speculation, insisting, 'Let's take one world at a time'? How many Robert Frosts thinking quietly, 'There may well be another chapter beyond this life, but we who are strong say not much about it now; we'll just wait and see'? How many Noel Cowards for whom this present chapter has been scarring enough that they mutter, 'One life's tough enough, don't threaten me with another'? How many Mark Twains shrugging, 'I've never heard one shred of reason why there should be an after-life, but somehow I fully expect one'? How many William James saying, 'You can't talk me out of it, for here, as I grow older, I'm just now getting fit to live'? Every form of belief, or lack of it, or need of it, will be mixed in with those whose thoughts about eternity are thoughts of friendly assurance, as one might think of home because of those who are there. Yet they will all be together in church on Easter, by their very presence doing some kind of honor to the deathless hope no man can quite escape. If the continuing appeal of Easter proved nothing else, it would underline how much is at stake for us all in the question. For you can't shrug this off as just a business of some-do-believe-it and some-don't.

"That's what Ed was really saying back there in his breakfast room, as he forgot the scalding water and stared at the lamp. He called it his 'faith,' but it wasn't a faith as yet. He had been shocked into realizing, as if for the first time, how much is at stake in this belief. His whole instinctive demand that life should make sense and should add up to something was speaking up. If people say, 'Oh, I can't take much stock in this future blessedness business,' then what in God's name can they take stock in? These quick years of getting ready to get ready to get ready—for what? Is all of it a prep school for something that never quite arrives? We never quite grow up, not really. You know it's all a quest for a happiness that never quite jells, a search for a knowledge never quite learned, a thirst for a meaning never fully found.

"Everything that Ed meant or felt in the word *justice* was speaking up. It won't do for any of us to say, 'Oh, I don't know, I've had a good life here, I've done as well as I deserved.' What about those who haven't? The sufferers who have nothing to show for their suffering, better men than we are who have drawn no breath without pain? What about the cornered, the deprived, the beaten, the shamed, the outraged? This is a world that does not pay its bills by the month and often not by the lifetime. We've never really cared about the heartbreak of mankind till we've at some time cried out with Dostoyevski, 'What keeps me going is that I believe like a child that suffering will be healed and made up for, that in the world's finale something so great will come to pass that it's going to suffice for all our hearts, for the comforting of all our sorrows, for the atonement of all the crimes of humanity. And I want to be there when suddenly everyone understands what it has all been for.'

"Any reality that Ed ever sensed in the name of God was speaking up in what he said. How are you going to come up with anything but a monstrous kind of God unless there is some permanence to personality? In Canon Streeter's great word, what defense, what possible defense will you arrange for this Power behind the universe, if He treats heroic souls like oyster shells at some drunken banquet, to be whisked from the table just to make room for the next course?

"Or, in Fosdick's simile, go down to the river in New York. Can't you tell a ferryboat from a seagoing ship? Ferryboats look like ferryboats; they were built to hug the shore.

But there are other ships with cargo in them, meant for the seven seas, size and tonnage and fuel that brand them as seagoing, meant to do business in deep waters. That's how it is with some people you've known: they're too big for oblivion; they're too important to stop—unless God's joking about it all! And what a monstrous joke that would be! Would Michelangelo have carved his figures on ice? Would the architect of the Parthenon have built it on quicksand? Would Raphael have painted his madonnas on Kleenex? Is God less the artist, less concerned with His handiwork? Is dust His only medium? Is He blowing mere bubbles when He brings to life the people we've known and loved and admired? If so, then don't call Him 'God'! Either forget Him or think up some harsh, bitter name for such a cosmic fraud! So the heart of man can argue, and always has.

"But that isn't a faith yet, Larry. The mind can know that there could be immortality, conscience can clamor that there should be, and love can insist that there must be. But that religion-in-the-raw must have an Easter to date from if it's ever to be more than a yearning, and something like a conviction, something worth calling a 'faith.'

"Dawn and a proclamation at a tomb, 'I know that ye seek Jesus which was crucified, He is not here, for He is risen as He said.' Easter doesn't argue; Easter invites. It invites us to realize that you and I can know it's Easter only if we, these centuries later, have some personal dealing with that same Power who brought Christ out of a grave and back into life to stay. On this the church stakes its whole reason for being. The same Power that on that day shattered death is now offered us to live by. To know Him—now forgiving us, strengthening us, bringing us again and again out of those tombs of the soul where we've buried our best, showing us how to believe and love and hope in spite of ourselves—to know God is to know that Easter was and is and shall be.

"Thomas à Kempis was thinking one day, 'If only I were sure of it, if only I were absolutely certain of it!' And a voice spoke quietly in his ear, 'Decide how you would live if you were absolutely certain of it; then try to live that way and see how much more certain you become.' That's the only way they'll know, Larry. It's the only way you and I can know. But has there ever been offered to mankind a belief more worth the trying?"

12

A Dream of Judgment

The last log in the fireplace had burned through and fallen onto the bed of coals beneath. Perhaps it was the tiny crash that had brought him back. Or perhaps it was Jo's presence, finally felt, that had reached him as she perched on the low fireplace bench watching him with concern as he sat in his favorite wing-back chair. She managed to keep the alarm out of her voice but the little furrow on her forehead, which was her hallmark of concern, was a deep cleft as she asked quietly, "Were you dreaming, Jack? You seemed to be talking in your sleep, but your eyes weren't quite closed. You had me worried."

Jack did not smile, as he normally would have, to reassure her. He was still under the spell of what he had seen, wherever he had been. He answered quietly and spoke slowly, "I suppose I must call it a dream, Jo. I don't know what else to call it. We call them daydreams when we stage them in some daytime reverie. And when we're asleep, of course, we know they were dreams after we awaken. We can often even see that they were just the problems of the day blown up to larger-than-life size, wearing masks so they will be allowed onstage in that strange corner of our minds where we keep a little theater always ready for the curtain to go up when our eyelids close.

"But we seem to have no agreed-upon name for the plots and scenes and fancies that come to us while we're still half awake. We can control these, compose them, usually direct them ourselves, although not so easily as daydreams. Yet sometimes they take over and build their own stage sets and write their own lines and direct their own plots. They can seem so much more real than so much we call real. Yet—how else can I say it, Jo?—here, tonight, before the fire, with you upstairs and the house quiet and the noises of the city outside muted, I began to think of that word *judgment*, and I dreamed a dream of judgment.

"I found myself walking near the end of a great bridge. Somehow the bridge itself, the clean beam and the curve of its balanced structure, reminded me of other bridges I had crossed at other times and other places. Yet this one seemed longer and higher in the air, spanning—oh, I couldn't estimate the distances. Once or twice I looked over the edge, and my view scanned only what appeared to be measureless deeps of mist and cloud. Once or twice I looked behind, and that end of the bridge was hidden in the pale, milky mists of twilight. I couldn't see from where I had come or how far.

"Ahead, the sunshine bathed the land where the bridge led. Blue sky was over the little town, and there was a feeling of bright early morning. The landscape tones of the woods and valleys were vivid blues and greens, so vivid I wondered why they did not sting my eyes. As I stepped off the bridge, the air was warm without heaviness yet fresh without chill. I remember feeling an odd kind of regret that I was dressed in the same old winter suit I had been wearing back there—wherever 'back there' was and whatever had happened. This seemed to be the sort of place where you'd feel more comfortable in new and different clothes.

"As so often holds true in dreams, I knew where I was

supposed to go without asking how I knew. The streets were empty but the village did not seem deserted or lonely. It was as if I had caught it at that precise moment before a little town awakens. At any time now people would begin to stir in the houses and would be up and about the demands of the morning. But I was headed for the courthouse square. I think I even remember feeling with some surprise the unforced vigor of my own pace. For that I credited the climate.

"The courthouse stood where I knew it would. As I turned the corner, I saw it dominating the town square, squat and blunt, its straight lines relieved only where the lawn around it boasted proud, unguessably old oak trees and even a light growth of hazels with their broad untrembling leaves. Again there was that sensation of something so familiar with all this strangeness. I hurried across the street and up the wide granite steps, for I knew that just inside the big outer door someone would be waiting for me in the hall outside the courtroom.

"And he was. He was leaning easily against the wall, hunched comfortably over his folded arms, until he heard me open the door. Then he came to attention. We walked toward each other, he gracefully, smiling cordially, but I clumsily, uncertainly, because for all his smile he was studying my face intently, the way an attending physician might study the face of a patient who has survived surgery and is coming out from under the anesthesia. I almost expected him to take my pulse as he took my hand in a strong grip. He said what would have seemed fatuous except in his richly modulated voice: 'Well, we've been expecting you.'

"I started to answer, then suddenly couldn't. His voice! Why, it had in it unmistakable overtones of half a dozen well-remembered voices. And the line of his jaw reminded me of—the way he thrust his hand out at an angle, so suddenly, was such a familiar gesture that the memory was an aching hurt. Above all, his eyes held me like the grip of something physical. Wide open, they were so dark a brown they seemed to be all pupil, witout an iris. The last time I had seen those eyes they had been filled with such pain and courage before they closed.

"He stepped back one step to let me study him more easily, and his smile was one of pleasure. 'I see you noticed the resemblances immediately. Well, that will please them all. They spent quite a while selecting me. No one who knew you back there can come, of course, until your trial's over and the verdict's handed down. But they're allowed to choose someone who'll meet you and prepare you for the trial.'

"Out of the hundred questions jostling around inside me and clamoring to be asked, the one which managed to get itself spoken was, 'Trial? What trial? Whose trial?'

"I couldn't complain with any fairness that he was in any way patronizing, but there was in his manner the unhurried patience which the honestly mature display with a blustering child as he answered, 'Oh, come now, play fair with your heart. Haven't you always known all your life back there, haven't you always somehow known that someday over here you would be judged?'

"I knew it was simply a chill of fear snatching at me for the first time, and I tried to keep my voice casual and controlled. Even to my ears, however, it sounded high pitched and thin, as if the very air we were breathing were more substantial than my voice. 'Look,' I let my exasperation have its head, 'I find it very difficult as a rational human being to take all this seriously. Finding myself suddenly on that bridge with no sensible explanation as to how or why; then homing it for this courthouse mirage and finding you waiting like some Virgil for some Dante, the charming, all-knowing guide to the other world—it's too hackneyed and storied and patterned! It smacks of all the folk myths I've ever heard. It's the stuff all the standard dreams are made of.'

"He wasn't smiling now, and I felt the reach of his concern again as he laid a hand on my arm. I almost shrank from the touch; the weight of just his hand was so heavy. 'Please,' he said, 'I know the shock of getting here suddenly. I know how long it takes to shed your long-practiced pose of, as you put it, a rational human being. But you'll have so much less time to wait to be ready for trial if you'll begin to realize it doesn't matter so much now what you can take seriously. What matters over here is in what way you can be taken seriously. As for legend and story, I don't think we've ever found one basic myth from back there that wasn't in some way a cue to reality, a hint of the way things really are.' He had taken my arm as we stepped across the hall and with a push of his free hand had opened the leather-padded door to the courtroom. We stepped inside.

"I was overcome for a moment at the sweep and size of the empty courtroom, the length of its aisles, the Gothic atmosphere. I'd never thought before how easily a courtroom could be made to resemble a church, with the benches as pews, the jury box as the choir, even the Judge's high bench gleaming austerely in the distance with its carved panels of golden oak, like some kind of high altar. And then I recognized it. What a subtle refinement of cruelty was this!

"I turned in anger. 'Say what you will, I can't appreciate this brand of theatrical you've dredged up out of my memory!' For all its impressiveness and far finer, grander scale, this courtroom was modeled on the one where, as a boy, I often watched my uncle preside, where so often I heard my—well, one even closer—plead to the jury, heard him with a boy's fear for him and pride in him. 'Is this your sense of humor over here?'

"He had seated himself on one of the empty benches. And even in my irritation some steady part of me took notice with what easy yet thoroughly masculine gracefulness he was mannered. 'Sit down,' he said, 'you may have quite a while to wait. The Great Judge can't be summoned by peevishness.

" 'Of course, this court was blueprinted from your memory. What did you expect? Or were you so silly as to expect nothing? Did you think Paul was playing with words? *Each shall be judged according to that particular light he was shown.* It ought to make you more at home. It should give you your first inkling that the place of judgment is always the hall of memories. But what puzzles us when we've been here awhile is how many of you are shocked, virtually outraged, to discover that there's any carryover between back there and over here. What warp in your proud little reasoning ever convinced you that even that first glimmer, that fragmentary initiation into life you had back there, had no meaning, was heading nowhere, was adding up to nothing? Your every instinct knew better than that.

" 'Please believe me,' he continued. 'You are now everything you've ever been, everything you've ever done. You are now every failure to be what you could have become and every failure to help another. There are some who come who expect the court to keep a little book of pluses and minuses, little black sins and little shining virtues. Why should the court keep books on you? You are your own ledger. Nothing is forgotten, not really. You're like some copper plate on which an etcher has scratched an unerasable design, the acid burning indelibly the pattern of all you've enjoyed and loved and trusted—yes, and all you've despised and hurt and despaired of.'

"I sat down heavily. All the stimulus of my anger had leaked away and left me limp. The bench felt hard. 'Who—who will prosecute me?'

" 'Why, you'll prosecute yourself. When you stand naked before the light of that bench, you'll accuse yourself and you'll plead your own guiltiness.'

" 'But who will speak in my defense?' "

"For the first time he seemed surprised. 'Oh, don't you know that? Don't you even know that?'

"And I was alone, in an empty courtroom—that is, if a room can be empty that seems crowded with witnesses, every healing or scalding memory. Then the light, so bright that it hurt my eyes, began to glow above the Judge's bench. I heard the crack of a gavel and a voice that called with no-nonsense briskness, 'Who brings the charges against the accused?'

"I was walking forward toward the bench, toward that light. I was hearing myself answer wearily, 'I charge the accused, Your Honor.'

"Again He called, 'Who knows the defendant and will speak in his defense?' And Someone had joined me there before the bench. A voice I had heard all my life, yet never listened to before, was answering, 'I know the defendant, Father, and I will speak in his defense.'

"But with that, the dream was over. I heard the log fall in the fireplace, and the house was quiet. You were sitting there, Jo, and I had no notion how long you had been there. So I didn't get to hear the testimony or the verdict. But someday I will. And you will, too.

"I suppose it's late, darling. Time for bed?"

notion of it, or description of it, or imagery about it. The diagrams and illustrations from Dante's *Inferno* have no more claim on our faith than the vulgar cartoons from the babblers of brimstone who have hurt this belief in its own house. I think we must even remember that Christ's own words about it were meant to be more pictorial than actual, to help us in our imaginations to see something we can't quite conceive. That's why He changed the pictures so often.

"By the way, it's a shocker to notice how often the so-called gentle Jesus did talk about hell—sometimes as a burning torment, but just as often as a sentence of exile, or a closed door you can't enter, or a welcome home you can't share; a being banished away from warmth and light; a cold, wandering, dark lostness. I doubt if much more is to be learned from Jesus' own word-pictures than from our puzzled acceptance of a dreadful possibility that's meant to seem terrible when thought about—and it's meant to be thought about.

"You see, if a game is played that's worth winning, it must be possible to lose that game, too; otherwise it's no true game, it's rigged. We believe life is worth living because it's a game worth winning; and the way it's lived has consequences. The direction we take has results, results that carry over and continue beyond the change of scenery we call *death*.

"Here's the way C. S. Lewis approached it a few years ago. I can't quote him exactly, but this is how he reasoned. Try to imagine a man who has made a career of treachery and cruelty, and has arrived at wealth and power by taking advantage of every decent trait of those he dealt with, even his family, even those who were once his friends. He has even sneered consistently at any goodness in his victims as so much spineless softheadedness. So he has crawled to his own apparent success over the broken hearts and lives and careers of others. Rather than mellowing, as we'd expect, he has silenced all pangs of remorse or conscience, and pictures himself as a model man who's been clever enough to outmaneuver God and the human race. He really enjoys, so far as he understands enjoyment, a good many years of the spendable dividends of ruthless self-centeredness. Then, with no change of heart whatsoever, he dies. Lewis's question is: What will you ask the God of justice, who really detests wrong, to do?

"Why, of course, it's an exaggerated picture! No, I've never personally known so monstrous a man, either. But that was done deliberately so that we wouldn't identify the description as anyone we know, because the moment you or I say of anyone we know, 'He deserves hell,' we're saying what no mortal dare say about another.

"But answer it—What would you ask God to do with such a man? Give him another chance? Why, God was trying to do that all the man's life, and he'd have none of it. Forgive him? Oh, God did that, from His side of things. But forgiveness is no blank check; it's a two-way traffic: it must be accepted as well as offered. This man refused to be forgiven. So what's God to do? Just go away and leave that man alone? You know, perhaps that's what He will do—just go away and leave the man all to himself. That just may be the hell of it! Forever and forever, with never, never an appeal from that sentence? I suspect that's a question we've never been equipped to ask or answer. I can imagine that Christ's comment might be, 'What's that to thee? Follow thou Me.' "

Jack was buttoning his coat and glancing in the mirror. Really not too bad a job, considering what Pete had to work with. Jo couldn't complain too much this time. He paid Pete and nodded to both men and went out.

The man in the chair scratched his jaw and said, "There you are, Pete. Just the way I've told you. That's the way they all are today. Never a straightforward answer to a simple question. That's why I haven't been near a church for twenty years." And he yawned and picked up his paper again, and turned to the last page to read the obituaries.